MICROPHONES–
How They Work &
How to Use Them

MICROPHONES–
How They Work &
How to Use Them
By Martin Clifford

TAB BOOKS
BLUE RIDGE SUMMIT, PA. 17214

FIRST EDITION

FIRST PRINTING—MAY 1977
SECOND PRINTING—OCTOBER 1979

Hardbound Edition: International Standard Book No. 0-8306-7875-1

Paperbound Edition: International Standard Book No. 0-8306-6875-6

Library of Congress Card Number: 77-79349

Cover Photo Courtesy of North American Phillips Corporation

Contents

Introduction

Introduction

Of all the components in a high-fidelity system the microphone is the least appreciated and the least understood. Practically an unwanted orphan in the high-fidelity sound hierarchy, the quality microphone for amateur recording use is a "Johnny come lately," a newcomer. This is not only an odd situation, but one that is inexplicable, for the microphone is the fountainhead, the source, the starting point of all recorded sound—without exception. Every bit of recorded tape, every phonograph record, every broadcast has a single, common ancestry—the *microphone*.

That this state of affairs is shocking is beyond question. It is only when we come to analyze the reasons behind it that we can first begin to understand why the microphone is the last arrival in a long progression of high-fidelity components.

Quality microphones have always been used in broadcasting stations and recording studios. Until just a few years ago, any musical group that wanted to "cut a record" had only one route and that was to use the services of a professional recording studio. It was in the studio that the would-be recordist received his first introduction to a complex maze of electronic instruments. Placed in a situation that was extremely confusing, the recordist had no choice but to be guided by studio directors and recording engineers. It was, and still is, an expensive bit of education, with no assurance of recording success. The recordist went in bewildered and came out clutching a precious master tape—still bewildered.

All that is now in the process of change, fortunately. At one time tape decks for in home use had severe limitations. And the microphones with which they were supplied came in the same category. But today a number of high-fidelity manufacturers are supplying tape decks for the amateur recordist that are professional in every sense of the word. They are electronically designed to produce recordings that are superb. And accompanying this upward movement in tape deck quality, the manufacturers of the software, the tapes, began to produce tapes with new formulations that extended frequency response and had much higher signal-to-noise ratios. Various noise reducing techniques also became part of the in-home recording scene.

The result of all this is that the recordist can now work in his own environment. Outboard mixers and equalizers and a full line of quality microphones and accessories now give him an opportunity to produce professional recordings. So what we have today is a growing hobby, one that has great appeal for the amateur and professional musician, or for the high-fidelity listener, or for anyone having an interest in recording sound. Further, there are now two types of tape decks that can be used for quality recording—the open reel and the cassette. Even 8 track cartridge units, once available as playback types only, are now being supplied with a record facility.

The manufacturers of the hardware, the various tape decks, and the manufacturers of the software, the various open reel, cassette and cartridge tapes, didn't waste any time in supplying the general public with detailed information on how best to use their devices. There is no shortage of advice on how to set up a recording facility. But they omit one important factor, undoubtedly the most important one—the microphone.

Although a tape deck for the amateur recordist can cost only 1/10 that of a studio unit, it can produce comparable quality results. And the tape being used with such tape decks is every bit as good as the tape used in studios. The difference in amateur versus recording in the studio is the use of cheap, poor-quality microphones, a lack of understanding on how to position microphones, and a general failure to appreciate what a microphone is and what it can do. The microphone is the first link in the recording chain. The amplifiers and speakers that follow the microphone can alter the sound or modify it in some way, but they cannot improve it.

The purpose of this book, then, is to supply you with practical working information about microphones. This book will not show you how to engineer a microphone, how to design one, or how to repair one. This book does explain what microphones are, how they work, and the different types available, with considerable emphasis on practical use.

No book writes itself, and this book is no exception. It is the collective effort of a large number of individuals, each of whom in his own way made a substantial contribution. Ideas and recommendations were made by the executives and engineers of AKG Akustiche U. Kino-Gerate GES. M.B.H. Vienna, specifically Dr. Rudolf Gorike, co-founder and Chief Scientist; Ing. Werner Fidi, Technical Director; Ing. Konrad Wolf, Supervisor, Condenser Microphone Development; Ing. Karl Peschel, Special Projects Engineering; and Ing. Norbert Sobol, Consulting Engineer.

This book is the end product of international cooperation. A special acknowledgment is due to AKG Acoutics, Mahwah, N.J. Help came in the form of discussions about microphones, technical literature, specification sheets, and encouragement. So a special vote of thanks must go to Andrew A. Brakhan, vice president; Robert W. Miller, Manager, Market Development; S. Richard Ravich, Marketing Manager; Geoffrey M. Langdon, Technical Manager; and Allan Smith, Acoustical Consultant, Stereosonic Laboratories.

Finally, there is always one man who sparks a project of this kind, who reads manuscripts and supplies advice, suggestions, guides, and corrections, always with a view to supplying the reader with a readable and practical work. In this case it is George A. Garnes, Director of Advertising, North American Philips Corporation, New York, N.Y., to whom cooperation was a word to be taken quite seriously.

To all of them, my thanks and appreciation.

Martin Clifford

Chapter 1
The World of Sound

THE WORLD OF SOUND

The input to every microphone (abbreviated as *mike*), no matter how it is designed or constructed, is *sound*. Before any microphone can function, before it can do the necessary work of converting sound-energy input to an electrical output, sound must be present.

The difficulty with sound is that it is so common. We are born hearing sounds and, except for those who have physiological defects, sound accompanies us throughout our lifetime. Sound is a necessary partner to one of our five senses—our sense of *hearing*. But because it is so much with us, we tend to take it for granted, perhaps not realizing it belongs to the energy family, a rather small group that includes heat energy, electrical energy, chemical energy, and mechanical energy.

We use sound for communications and for pleasure. We are perhaps not so critical when we use sound for communications, for here the criterion is intelligibility, not authentic reproduction. With high-fidelity music we are more concerned with an exact replica of the original sound source. That concern is a practical one, for reproduced sound that is distorted not only produces listening fatigue, but diminishes our enjoyment of music.

Learning more about sound is essential if we are to manipulate it, if we are to understand why microphones work

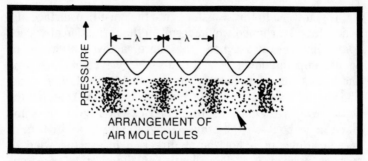

Fig. 1-1. Graphic representation of a sound wave. The distance from one peak to the next is a wavelength, represented by the Greek letter lambda (λ). The scattered dots below the sound wave represent the arrangement of air molecules.

the way they do, if we are to appreciate how we are to select particular types of microphones and position them effectively. The way we can do that is to understand this component, to know just what *sound* is, the relationships of sounds to each other and to microphones, and the behavior of sound under various conditions.

WHAT IS SOUND?

We all know what sound is and that's why it is so difficult to define. Sound is generated when we displace the normal random motion of air molecules. If you clap your hands or bow a musical instrument, the result is an alternate rarefaction (expansion) and compression of air molecules, with large groups of molecules forming bunches and fewer molecules between these bunches. Sound travels as a wave (Fig. 1-1). A wavelength is the distance from the peak of one sound wave to the peak of the next, represented by the Greek letter *lambda* (λ). An ocean wave, for example, contains a large amount of water rising to form some sort of peak, followed by a trough, then another peak and another trough. More elegantly, the sound can be defined as consisting of longitudinal pressure waves in the air, with alternate regions of high and low pressure—high where we have larger numbers of air molecules, low where the number of air molecules is fewer. Sound is a pressure increase and decrease above and below a barometric mean. The air particles compress and become more dense and alternately disperse, but they generally remain in the same general area in which they were originally at rest. Sound energy is transmitted as variations in pressure.

If you were to throw a stone into the unruffled surface of a pond, the disturbance would result in the formation of waves. Some distance away, near the shore, a toy boat would be bounced up and down. Now it takes energy even to move a toy and in this case that energy was supplied by the falling stone. The energy was transmitted from the stone to the boat, but the actual waves themselves remained essentially in the same place. The boat on the waves moves only up and down. It doesn't move in a horizontal direction unless the wind or current pushes it independently of the vertical pressure movements.

SOUND AND ITS TRAVELS

Sound can travel through liquid and solid bodies, through water, or steel, and other substances.

'Sound' carries an implication that it is something we can hear, in short, that it is audible. However, sound exists above the threshold of our hearing. We call it ultrasound. And it also exists below our hearing range and is known as infrasound.

In air, sound travels at a speed of about 1130 feet per second. If an auditorium is large enough, people in that auditorium will hear the same sound at different times. The time separation, of course, is quite short. Sound moves through water about four times as fast as it does through air; through iron its speed becomes about 14 times as rapid. Send sound through a rubber band and it moves along at a speed of about 131 feet per second. Sound, however, will not travel through a vacuum.

PRODUCTION OF SOUND

Any vibrating object can act as a sound source and produce a sound wave, and the greater the surface area the object presents to the air the more it can move. The object could be the vibrating string of a violin, a weak sound at best, but considerably reinforced by the vibrating wood body of the violin. It can be produced by a slap, or a dropped plate, or a bat striking a ball. The compressions and rarefactions of the air molecules are pressure variations that correspond to the vibrations of the sound source. Where the molecules of air are bunched together, the air pressure is above normal. In between the larger-than-normal groups of air molecules we have lower air pressure simply because we have fewer molecules. This condition will continue to exist as long as the original sound source continues vibrating. When it stops, the air molecules distribute themselves more or less equally, the pressure differences between groups of molecules disappear, and we no longer hear sound.

When a sound is produced by a source, the air molecules around the source are disturbed; that is, they are moved out of their random scattered condition. Their normal pattern of approximately equal distribution is changed.

The disturbance of air molecules around a sound isn't restricted to a single source. You could have two sound sources more or less immediately adjacent, and the air molecules around each of these sources would be disturbed by each of them. In other words, the air can support a number of independent sound waves produced at the same time.

TYPES OF SOUND VIBRATION

Musical *tones* are produced by regular vibrations. Because of its orderliness, we find these tones pleasant. *Noise* produces irregular vibrations. The variations in air pressure are random and our sense of hearing interprets them as unpleasant.

A musical *note* consists of a fundamental wave and a number of overtones, called *harmonics*. The composite waveform comprising the fundamental and its harmonics can look quite irregular, with many sharp peaks and valleys, and yet the fundamental tone and each harmonic is made up of a very regularly shaped waveform. Our ears, apparently, are able to recognize the regularity of the individual waves in such a complex waveform and are both pleased and satisfied.

While we can describe sound as the result of a variation in air pressure, it does have three fundamental characteristics. These are *pitch*, *timbre*, and *loudness*. Every sound has a definite frequency, a recognizable character. We can identify a sound as being produced by a violin, the human voice, or a trumpet. Sound is also recognized by its strength compared to other sounds.

PITCH

Pitch is the fundamental or basic tone of a sound and is determined by the *frequency* of that tone. The frequency of a wave is a measure of the number of complete waves per second. The greater the number of waves per second, the higher the frequency, that is, the higher the pitch. *Treble* tones have a much higher frequency than *bass* tones.

The fundamental or basic tone is sometimes called the *first harmonic*. However, it is the harmonics or overtones of the fundamental that supply the identifying characteristic of a sound and which enable us to distinguish between two tones having the same fundamental frequency but played on different musical instruments.

We don't always refer to the pitch of a sound, but may group the pitch into general classifications such as *bass*, *midrange* and *treble*, an arrangement quite commonly used in connection with high-fidelity systems.

The sounds produced by the tympani are high pitched; those made by the longer pipes of the organ are low pitched. Instead of referring to an entire range, such as bass, we can specify a single pitch. *A* above *middle C* on the piano has a frequency of 440 Hertz—that is, 440 complete cycles or waves per second.

The full range of any musical instrument, such as the piano, is from the pitch or frequency of the lowest tone it can produce to that of the highest. The range of human hearing, our ability to hear from the lowest pitch to the highest, encompasses all musical instruments plus the human voice. This doesn't mean sounds do not exist outside our hearing range. They do, but their pitch may be so low or so high that we cannot hear them. And not all human beings have the same hearing range. Human hearing has an average range of about 10 octaves.

WHAT HAPPENS TO THE SOUND?

As a sound leaves its source, such as a musical instrument, it spreads out, or *diffuses*. The entire region of sound could be called a *sound field* with the microphone immersed in that field. The space occupied by the microphone compared to the total sound field is small. Further, only a small section of the microphone is receptive to sound or is affected by it.

The sound that leaves a source uses up most of its energy in heating the air through which it moves. The amount of heat is small and the volume over which it is distributed is rather large. You cannot detect any heat difference by inserting your

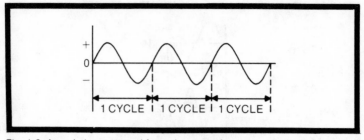

Fig. 1-2. A cycle is measured from the start of one wave to the beginning of the next. Frequency is measured in cycles per second. If three cycles are completed in one second, the frequency is three cycles per second or three Hertz (3 Hz).

hand between the sound source and the microphone. Sounds having a higher pitch diminish much more quickly over a given distance than do sounds of a lower pitch.

FREQUENCY

When sound energy is converted to its equivalent in electrical energy, the electrical output is an alternating current or alternating voltage waveform. The wave, known as a *cycle* (Fig. 1-2), consists of a pair of alternations, one of which is regarded as positive, the other as negative. Each alternation is half of a full cycle. The *frequency* is the total number of *completed* waveforms or cycles per second, including both the negative and positive half-cycles. At one time, frequency was measured in cycles per second, or cps. The Hertz, as indicated earlier, is now designated as the cycle per second. Abbreviated as Hz, 30 Hz means 30 complete cycles per second. The letter k is used to indicate a multiplier of 1000, so 1000 Hz can also be written as 1 kHz.

The fundamental AC waveform, called a *sine wave*, is shown in Fig. 1-3. The horizontal line drawn through the waveform separates the upper or *positive* (+) half from the lower or *negative* (−) half. With an increase in frequency, there are more cycles per second. A *pure* tone, a tone having no harmonics or overtones, appears as a sine wave. Pure tones, except when used to achieve special effects, are boring.

Harmonics

Harmonics or *overtones* are multiples of the fundamental frequency (Fig. 1-4). The tone of a musical instrument having a fundamental frequency of 250 Hz could have a second

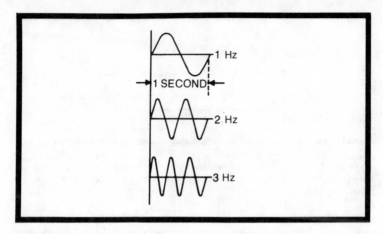

Fig. 1-3. As the frequency increases, there are more complete waves per second. The top drawing is 1 Hz, the center is 2 Hz, and the bottom is 3 Hz. The pitch of a sound increases with frequency. Bass tones are low frequency; treble tones are much higher in frequency.

harmonic or overtone at 500 Hz, a third harmonic at 750 Hz, a fourth harmonic at 1 kHz, and so on.

As we get beyond one of the upper-order harmonics, such as the fifth, the amplitude or strength of such overtones is quite small. The fundamental and its harmonics combine to produce complex waveforms. It is these waveforms that give

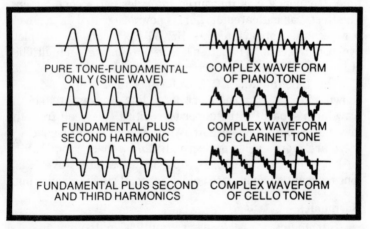

Fig. 1-4. Various types of waveforms. Harmonics are multiples of the fundamental frequency. They may be either odd- or even-numbered harmonics.

each tone its particular character. It enables us to distinguish between a tone produced on a piano and a tone of identical frequency made by a guitar or some other instrument.

Range of Musical Instruments

The fundamental range of musical instruments, as shown in Fig. 1-5, is quite limited. At the low frequency end, there are

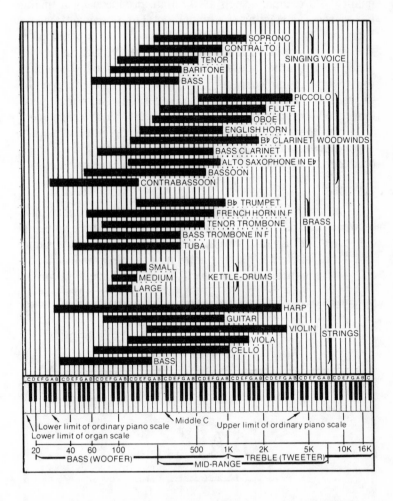

Fig. 1-5. The fundamental range of musical instruments is quite limited. This graphic representation illustrates ranges of fundamental components of tones for the principal musical instruments and voices. (Copyright by Ziff-Davis Publishing Company. Reprinted from Jan. 1976 Stereo Review by permission.)

very few musical instruments that have the capability of producing tones below 50 Hz. The human voice does not go much below 70 Hz, while at the high-frequency end all musical instruments and the voice are below 5 kHz in fundamental frequency.

While it is the fundamental frequency that determines the pitch of a tone, it is the harmonics that add richness and quality. Pure tones (such as the tone produced by a tuning fork)—tones consisting of a fundamental only—make tiresome listening. The number of harmonics produced depends on a variety of factors, whether the instrument is percussive or wind, for example, and also on playing technique. A violinist controls harmonic content by the movement of his fingers. In the case of the flute, playing it softly results in an almost pure tone, as shown in the top drawing of Fig. 1-6. With louder tones, however, there are more harmonics. So our enjoyment of a particular tone depends not only on the number of harmonics produced, but on the variation in the quantity of harmonics.

TIMBRE

That character of a sound which enables us to distinguish between different musical instruments, including the voice, is called *timbre*. Even if two instruments are playing the same tone—that is, each is playing notes having the same frequency and at the same loudness level—the notes have a different

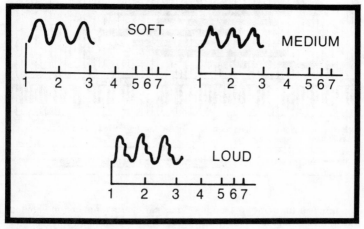

Fig. 1-6. The playing technique determines the harmonic content of the tone produced by a flute. The louder the tone, the greater the number of harmonics.

sound. Each musical instrument has its own particular pattern of overtones.

Overtones or harmonics (also called *partials* or *partial tones*) are classified into two groups: *odd* and *even*. An even harmonic is one that is an even-order multiple of the fundamental frequency (f) of the tone. A tone of 440 Hz has its second harmonic at 880 Hz. The next even-order harmonic would be four times the fundamental, or $4 \times 440 = 1760$ Hz. If we call the fundamental fl, the second harmonic would be $2 \times fl$ or $2fl$, the fourth harmonic would be $4fl$, and so on. The odd-order harmonics would be $3fl$, $5fl$, and so on. If the fundamental is 400 Hz, the third harmonic, $3fl$, is $400 \times 3 = 1200$ Hz.

The various tones produced by musical instruments differ in two respects: in the total number of overtones they yield, and in whether those overtones are odd or even, or both. An instrument such as the violin supplies a fundamental plus odd and even overtones. A trumpet produces a fundamental plus odd overtones. The fundamental frequency is the basic pitch. If a note has five overtones, each higher-frequency overtone is usually (but not always) weaker than its predecessor. Thus, the second harmonic could be weaker than the fundamental, the third harmonic weaker than the second, and so on.

The total number of harmonics supplies the *character* of a tone. If a tone is accompanied by a large number of harmonics, we hear it as bright or brilliant; if accompanied by a few number of overtones it sounds restrained, muted, or mellow. Some people even refer to it as dull.

This characteristic of sound gives us a clue for aurally determining the functioning of a microphone. If the preamplifier and power amplifier following the microphone have an adequate frequency response—and good-quality amplifiers go beyond the outermost limits of human hearing—then our inability to distinguish between wood instruments and string instruments is an indication that the overtones are either not being reproduced or are being distorted.

LOUDNESS

Our ears aren't linear devices. We are most sensitive to tones in the middle frequencies, with decreasing sensitivity to those having relatively lower and higher frequencies.

Loudness and volume are not the same, as evidenced by the fact that a high-fidelity receiver will have both a loudness and a volume control. A volume control is used to adjust the overall sound level over the entire frequency range of the audio spectrum. A volume control is not frequency or tone selective, or at least it shouldn't be. When you advance the volume control in a receiver all tones are increased in level.

A more correct name for the loudness control would be "physiologically correct loudness contour compensation." This control is used to compensate for our hearing—a hearing that is relatively insensitive to bass and treble tones when the overall volume is very soft. The loudness control, or switch, overcomes this hearing characteristic by boosting these extreme sound ranges at low volume settings. The loudness control isn't required when listening at normal or high volume levels.

This situation applies not only to recorded music, but to live music as well. You can easily observe the difference in sound quality of an approaching marching band, depending on how near or far the band may be. At a distance, the music may sound somewhat flat, but it is much richer sounding when the musicians parade directly past you.

Volume has two important characteristics. The first is its *dynamic range*, extending from the threshold of hearing to the threshold of pain. The other characteristic is the *relationship of sound to time*. The chart in Fig. 1-7 is a comparison of the relative volume levels or ordinary sounds. The threshold of hearing is zero decibels (abbreviated dB) and the threshold of pain is 130 decibels. The decibel is a unit of comparative measurement, explained in more detail later in the book.

Figure 1-8 shows the curves of the thresholds of audibility and feeling. The encircled area is called the *auditory-sensation* area and includes all audible tones of any frequency and intensity. The curves also show that the thresholds for music are more restricted than those for speech.

Thresholds of Audibility and Feeling

What you can hear depends on your age, sex, and the physical condition of your ears and brain. While the audio spectrum is assumed to have a range of 20 Hz to 20 kHz, few of us have a hearing capability that goes down to 20 Hz, and equally few can really hear as high as 20 kHz. The pipe organ has a possible range below 20 Hz, while the bottom frequency of the contrabassoon is just a bit above 30 Hz; but even so, very little music is written for such low frequencies. Natural sounds include hardly any low frequencies and, as a matter of fact,

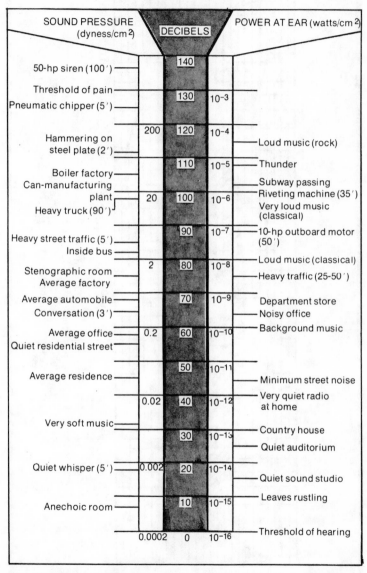

Fig. 1-7. Relative loudness levels of common sounds. (Copyright 1976 by the Ziff-Davis Publishing Company. Reprinted from Jan. 1976 Stereo Review by permission.)

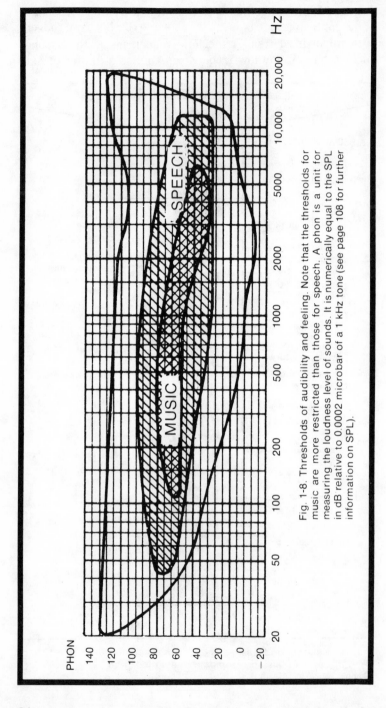

Fig. 1-8. Thresholds of audibility and feeling. Note that the thresholds for music are more restricted than those for speech. A phon is a unit for measuring the loudness level of sounds. It is numerically equal to the SPL in dB relative to 0.0002 microbar of a 1 kHz tone (see page 108 for further information on SPL).

what you will find among the very low frequencies is just disturbing noise. At the high end, the piccolo and the violin have fundamentals that are lower than 5 kHz, but the harmonics of musical instruments are substantially higher.

Useful Frequency Range for Microphones

Consequently, the useful frequency range for microphones seems to be from about 50 Hz to 15 kHz. You will sometimes see a specification indicating a response of 20 Hz to 20 kHz, but most microphones are within more practical limits.

As you reduce the sound level more and more you will reach a level at which sound perception will stop. This is the threshold at which you will hear no sound, referred to as the *threshold of audibility*. The threshold of audibility depends on frequency; the sound pressure at the threshold of audibility differs substantially.

Going to the other extreme, sound can be made so loud that our perception of it turns into feeling. This upper limit is called the *threshold of feeling*, also known as the *threshold of pain*. Some rock concerts are capable of approaching this level.

THE OCTAVE

A doubling of frequency is called an *octave*. From 30 Hz to 60 Hz could be called an octave, since 30×2 (or 30 doubled) equals 60. We could regard 60 Hz to 120 Hz as still another octave, and so on.

Table 1-1. Determining Octaves and Frequency Ranges

Frequency Range, Hz	Octave
16 to 32	first
32 to 64	second
64 to 128	third
128 to 256	fourth
256 to 512	fifth
512 to 1024	sixth
1024 to 2048	seventh
2048 to 4096	eighth
4096 to 8192	ninth
8192 to 16,384	tenth

We do not start with 0 Hz, for this is actually a direct current or voltage such as that supplied by a battery, for example. Considering music, 32 Hz is a practical beginning; but we can start with 16 Hz as a bottom limit. If we select 16 Hz as our starting point, we can then have 10 octaves, up to approximately 16 kHz. Insufficient pickup by a microphone of certain octaves, or overemphasis of other octaves, will alter the sound output of the microphone.

The 10 octaves in Table 1-1 are of particular interest, since they roughly represent the range of human hearing capability. There are sounds below 16 Hz, of course, and above 16 kHz, but most of us cannot hear them and, as a matter of fact, 16 Hz and 16 kHz could be considered the outermost hearing limits.

What we have, then, is the possible range of sound pickup by a microphone—10 octaves. This is a tremendous range. A lens in a camera works with light instead of sound, but both light and sound are forms of energy. Yet the lens can confine itself to just one octave—from 4000 Angstroms (the Angstrom is a unit of light measurement) to 8000 Angstroms. Motion-picture sound works with a range of about six octaves, and for telephone conversations the range is even narrower, just three to four octaves.

A lens, or course, is just a collector of light, just as the microphone is a collector of sound. But the similarity ends there, for the microphone is a *transducer*, something the lens is not. The microphone must not only collect sound, but transduce or convert it to an equivalent form of electrical energy. A lens receives light, but its output is still light. Although a microphone is sometimes compared to a lens, the microphone has the far more difficult job. For high-fidelity use, a range of 9 to 10 octaves is quite an accomplishment.

CHARACTERISTICS OF THE SOUND SPECTRUM

The first two octaves, 16 Hz to 64 Hz, contain the bass tones. Sounds in this region can consist of tones produced by the pipe organ, the piano, and the harp. It is in these first two octaves that we encounter troubles with *hum*. The frequency of the average power-line voltage is 60 Hz (in some foreign localities it is 50 Hz). The hum produced by a defect in a fluorescent fixture can have a frequency of 60 Hz; but if it isn't a pure tone, that is, one without harmonics, then you may be hearing the second harmonic at 120 Hz. Turning off the lights is one solution to this difficulty if you notice hum during playback.

Bass tones supply richness, depth, and power. If a bass tone has a very low frequency and is strong enough, we may *feel* rather than hear it. Even when bass tones occur only momentarily, they manage to set up a pleasing balance with higher frequency tones. Without them, higher tones, those in the upper midrange and treble range, will seem stronger than they really are.

While noise can occur anywhere in the audio spectrum, certain noises make their home in the bass tones. Street noises, various noises inside the home, and other sounds we normally disregard and aren't conscious of hearing, can show up in the first two octaves.

The third and fourth octaves, from 64 Hz to 256 Hz, contain the frequencies that supply musical tempo. It is in these frequencies that you will hear orchestral rhythm. Drum beats and piano tones appear in these octaves. The fifth, sixth, and seventh octaves are known as the midrange frequencies, or more commonly just as the *midrange*. In this frequency range, 256 Hz to 2048 Hz, is that part of the sound spectrum to which the ear is quite sensitive. *Middle C* on the piano comes near the bottom of the midrange, and the majority of musical intruments have either their fundamental tones or first harmonics here.

The remaining sounds are in the 7th to 10th octaves. Male speech is about 3 kHz to 6 kHz, while female tones are higher by an octave.

CHARACTERISTICS OF SOUND

A sound does not reach its maximum level instantaneously. It takes some time for it to do so, however short that time may be. And after reaching its maximum level, neither does it decrease immediately to zero. The sound may be sustained for a while, if the sound-energy source remains active. Finally, it takes time for the sound to decay, that is, to approach and reach a zero sound level. Figure 1-9 shows this triple characteristic. The *attack* time is the time it takes the sound to reach its peak. *Sustain* is the level maintained by the sound source. (Note there may be a dropoff from the peak). Finally, there is a *decay* time, during which the sound drops to zero.

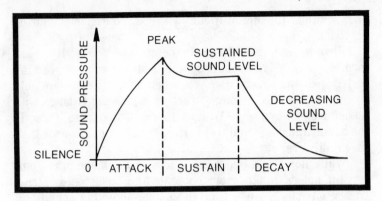

Fig. 1-9. Three characteristics of a sound wave include attack time, sustain time, and decay time.

Sustain time can be very short or it can be prolonged. With a piano, for example, using the pedal can sustain a tone after the piano key has been struck and released. Figure 1-10 shows quite a prolonged sustain time (in this example, almost two seconds). The human voice can sustain a tone, but the decay time will usually be short. The decay time of a guitar (Fig. 1-11) is rather long. It is these three characteristics—attack, sustain, and decay—that contribute to musical-instrument personality and makes each musical instrument so different.

One of the most beautiful aspects of the human voice is its ability to alter any one of the three characteristics of sound. It can reach maximum level quickly or slowly. It can sustain a tone for a longer or shorter time. And it can make decay time gradual or sharp.

Figure 1-12 contains graphic representations of the ways the human voice can control sound. In the first drawing (A),

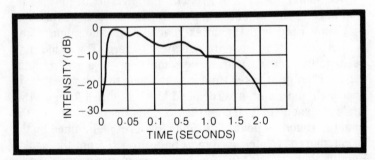

Fig. 1-10. With the sustain pedal depressed, a piano tone can last for a long time. In this example it is almost two seconds.

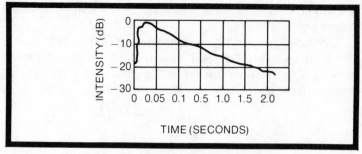

Fig. 1-11. Decay of a guitar tone is rather long.

the attack time is very short. The voice tone reaches its peak rather quickly, with sustain time and decay time merging into each other. In this instance the sound decreases smoothly and gradually.

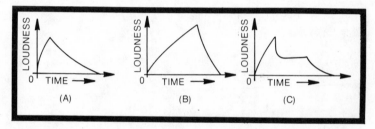

Fig. 1-12. Three variations in the wave of a tone: sharp attack, gradual decay (A); gradual attack, sharp decay (B); sharp attack, sharp partial decay, followed by sustain and then gradual decay (C). Many other variations are possible.

In the center illustration (B), the voice reached its peak slowly, but sustain and decay are quite rapid. In the final drawing (C), the peak is reached quite quickly, followed by a

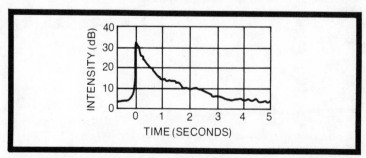

Fig. 1-13. Piano tone is percussive with an extremely short rise time.

quick decrease. The note is then sustained for a time, and then decays gradually.

Percussive instruments are characterized by very sharp attack times, with the result that the tone reaches its peak extremely quick. Like the guitar, the piano has a rather long decay time, as shown in Fig. 1-13.

Chapter 2
Meet the Mike

MEET THE MIKE

The idea behind the microphone is simple, for all a microphone, any microphone, is required to do is change one form of energy to another. The *Encyclopedia Britannica* defines the microphone as a "device for converting acoustic power into electric power which has essentially similar wave characteristics."

A telephone can meet this requirement, so one of the basic parts of a telephone is a microphone. But what we take for granted today was quite a problem about a hundred years ago. At the Centennial Exposition (Philadelphia, 1876), Alexander Graham Bell demonstrated a liquid microphone. He put a metal wire, about a fraction of an inch thick, into water mixed with acid. At the other end of the wire he attached a diaphragm that could be vibrated by voice waves. The resultant jiggling of the wire in the water varied an electric current that was made to flow through the diaphragm, the wire, and the acid/water mixture.

Bell was the inventor of the first telephone that could carry the human voice for some distance so it was still intelligible to the listener at the other end. Despite Hollywood, though, he wasn't the inventor of the telephone and didn't even give the component its name. Philip Reis, of Friedrichsdorf, Germany, not only constructed the first telephone (in 1861), but named it as well. And Elisha Gray of Chicago was able to build a short-distance telephone in 1873. Alexander Graham Bell didn't come along with his telephone until 1876. So much for laurels, glory, and who deserves the credit—they all do.

Microphones are associated with telephones because you must have a microphone before you have a telephone. The early microphones used by Bell, Reis, and Gray were attic-inventor contraptions. They worked, but you wouldn't want to use any of them to call your home. Credit for the invention of the microphone goes to Prof. D.E. Hughes, an Englishman, who finally came through with one that was eminently practical, and he is regarded as its inventor. This took place in 1878 and, oddly, microphones had already been in use for almost 20 years.

THE MICROPHONE AND ITS RELATIVES

The microphone is a strange and wonderful instrument, even more so when you consider its family tree. The microphone is directly related to speakers, for in some cases (as in intercoms), the microphone also works as a speaker. Since the microphone is a *transducer*—a device that changes one form of energy to another—it is first cousin to storage batteries, motors, generators, piezoelectric crystals, and the electric light.

This disparate group is related in the sense that they are all energy converters. A battery changes chemical energy to electrical energy, the motor converts electrical energy to mechanical energy, and so on. What we require of the microphone is quite simple—to change sound energy to its electrical equivalent. Electrical, *not* electronic. We ask it to perform like a battery or a generator, that is, to produce an electric current.

WHAT IS A MICROPHONE?

A microphone is basically a collector of sound, taking acoustical energy input and converting it to electrical energy. The problem is that the acoustical energy contained in our voices or in musical instruments is full of sudden starts and stops. The piano, a percussive instrument, is easily capable of going from a condition of *no sound* to *peak sound* in almost no time at all. And the sound level of some instruments, as well as the human voice, can decrease extremely rapidly. So one of the required characteristics of a microphone is that it must be

Fig. 2-1. The simplest microphone is a tin can with one of its covers removed. Two such cans connected with a length of string can transmit sounds up to about 20 feet.

responsive to rapid changes in acoustical energy. This is somewhat like asking an automobile to move from *rest* to 70 mph, down to 30, up to 45, and down to 10, practically instantaneously. One of the problems the auto has in doing this is a law of Nature which insists that a body at rest prefers remaining at rest and a body in motion prefers staying in motion. More elegantly known as a *law of inertia*, it is as applicable to microphones as it is to cars. The comparison isn't quite fair, however, for the mass of a car is tremendous in comparison with the moving element of the microphone.

MAKING A MICROPHONE

The simplest microphone you can imagine consists of a pair of tin cans (Fig. 2-1), each having a cover removed. Any pair salvaged from the kitchen will do. Punch a hole in the center of each can and insert a length of string in the ends. Just tie a knot on the inside of the can so the string cannot come loose. With this arrangement and with the string kept taut, you can transmit your voice over a distance of about 20 feet.

In this setup each tin can works both as a microphone and a speaker. The acoustical energy going into one of the cans causes the bottom cover to vibrate. This vibration is transferred to the string and travels to the other can. The bottom of the second can will be caused to vibrate by the

34

energy it receives from the string. But in vibrating, the can cover will move air back and forth, in step with the sound going into the first can. This air movement, upon reaching your ear, is converted into sound.

What we have here is a transducer, changing sound energy to mechanical energy at one end, then converting that mechanical energy back to sound energy at the other.

Granted that this is a very crude system, that the string must be kept dry, that it must be kept tight, that the communications distance is very small, and that the quality of the sound reproduction is terrible. All this is beside the point right now. What *is* important is to realize that this device tells us that acoustical energy can be changed into some other form and that the acoustical energy can be made to work as a control. In this example, the energy produced by the human voice caused the cover of a tin can to vibrate. Not just to vibrate, mind you, but to vibrate in step with the variations and changes in the human voice.

There is one other problem presented by the tin-can microphone. It seduces us into taking a completely wrong path toward the development of a microphone, for while it converts sound energy into some other form, there is no way in which we can modify, improve, or amplify that other form. We *can* change or amplify an electrical form, however, so our search for a practical microphone must take a path in which sound energy is converted to electrical energy.

THE VARIABLE RESISTOR MICROPHONE

Theoretically, at least, it isn't at all difficult to design a microphone which will change acoustic energy to electrical energy. As a first approach, consider Fig. 2-2. Here we have a variable resistor connected to a battery. Whenever an electrical current flows through a resistor, a voltage appears across it. The variable resistor R1 is equipped with a knob, so we can change the amount of current at will, just as rapidly as we can twirl the knob of R1. But as we do so, the current flowing through the next resistor will also vary. This produces a changing voltage across resistor R2.

But now we have another requirement. We must be able to turn the knob on R1 exactly in step with the variations in sound. A large current would correspond to a loud sound; a weak current would be equivalent to a weak sound. We could

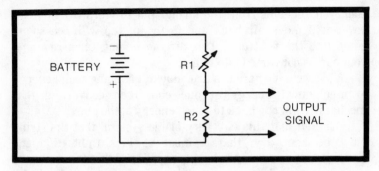

Fig. 2-2. Preliminary steps in making a microphone. R1 and R2 are resistors. The arrow through R1 indicates that it is variable; it has a knob to change its resistance. In turn, this varies the amount of current flow, through the circuit. The varying current through R2 produces a changing voltage across it. This becomes the output signal voltage.

then take the varying voltage produced across resistor R2 and connect it to an audio amplifier as indicated in Fig. 2-3, thereby strengthening the voltage produced by the "microphone," ultimately leading the voltage from the amplifier into a speaker. At the speaker, the reverse process would take place. Our electrical energy would be converted into acoustic energy and we would hear our original sound, considerably amplified.

Theoretically, this microphone would work. From a practical viewpoint it is impossible, however. There is no way in which we could manually rotate the knob on variable resistor R1 so as to follow the lightning speed of changes in sound. However, we could do so if we could manage to make the acoustic energy act as the control element. Instead of turning the knob manually, we should let the acoustic energy

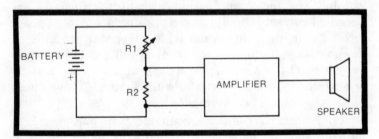

Fig. 2-3. If you could manage to rotate the knob on resistor R1 in step with the sound, you would hear an amplified version of the sound from the speaker.

do the turning. So now that we know the problem, all we need to do is to solve it.

THE CARBON MICROPHONE

The two microphones just described—the tin-can version and the knob-controlled type—aren't as ludicrous as they might appear. Based on the earlier definition of microphones, that is just what they are, for they are transducers, changing one form of energy to another. They both have serious faults, however, which preclude giving them further consideration. The arrangement using the variable resistor fails because the current flowing through it must be controlled manually, rather than by acoustic energy. The tin-can microphone fails because it is physical movement only and does not use an electric current. We have no way of using electricity to strengthen the sound signal.

The *carbon* microphone overcomes both of these objections, and while its design and concept are as outlandish as the tin-can microphone and the variable-resistor microphone, it nevertheless does work and has practical applications.

Figure 2-4 shows two views of the general arrangement of this microphone. The unit consists of a small cylinder, known as a *button*, packed with tiny granules of carbon. Pressing against the button containing the carbon granules is a *diaphragm*, a metallic disc supported only around its circumference.

Carbon is a conductor of electrical currents, so we now have a complete current path, as shown by the arrows in the lower drawing. You can trace this current path by starting at the minus terminal of the battery, marked with a minus (−) sign, moving up through the diaphragm, then through the carbon granules, through the resistor marked *R*, and finally back to the battery. This is a simple, straightforward circuit and the current that flows in it, supplied by the battery, is direct current (DC).

The diaphragm, or microphone element, just a thin, very flexible circular metallic plate, is held tightly in place by a rather thick support. While the plate cannot move at its periphery because it is fastened, the center of the plate can move. It will do so when you bring it close to your mouth and talk into it. The energy of your voice, impinging on the

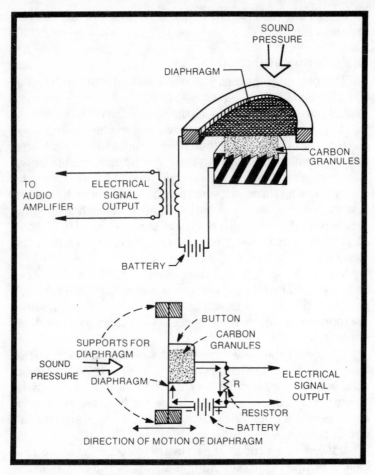

Fig. 2-4. Basic structure of the carbon microphone.

diaphragm, will cause it to vibrate in step with your voice. When it does so, it will move toward and away from the button containing the carbon granules, compressing them when the diaphragm moves inward, giving the granules a chance to separate when the diaphragm moves outward. But the action here is exactly the same as that of the variable resistor shown earlier in Fig. 2-2, with one difference, however, and quite a significant difference at that. In Fig. 2-4 the resistance is controlled by the energy in the sound reaching the diaphragm. There is no need for manual control, for now the voice or musical-instrument sounds determine the resistance of the granules in the button. When the granules are compacted, the resistance is lowered; when the granules are not pressed together, the resistance increases. And, of course, there are all sorts of variations between these two extremes. But as the resistance varies, so does the flow of current. The higher the resistance, the smaller the current, and vice versa. But this current, in flowing through resistor R, produces a varying voltage across R, a voltage that fluctuates in step with the sounds reaching the diaphragm. Because it follows the variations in sound presented to the microphone diaphragm, we refer to it as an audio voltage. It increases and decreases when the sound pressure increases and decreases. When the sound has abrupt starts and stops, so does the audio voltage.

The carbon microphone, one of the earliest microphone types, and still widely used today, has one tremendous advantage. It proves that a microphone can be a practical reality. It demonstrates that a microphone can be acoustically controlled. However, it is noisy and will not respond to other than a limited range of sound frequencies. Also, its diaphragm must be tightly stretched. This limits its possible movement, thereby reducing the electrical output level. Still another problem of the carbon microphone is the size of its diaphragm. The diaphragm should be small compared to the wavelengths of sound that reach it. And this is precisely why a loudspeaker makes such a poor microphone. The function of a speaker is opposite that of a microphone, for it must push air instead of being pushed by it. So for a speaker, large surface area is important.

IMPEDANCE

The word *impedance* is one you will often hear used in connection with microphones. All it means is total opposition to the flow of current. High impedance means large opposition; low impedance means smaller opposition. Impedance is no indication of quality; rather, it is just a fact of electrical behavior. As a general rule, low impedance means large current flow; high impedance smaller current flow. The basic unit of impedance is the *ohm* (abbreviated Ω), just as the inch is a unit of measurement for a ruler. Actual values of impedance for microphones aren't always specified exactly. Rather, general terms, such as *low impedance* or *high impedance*, are used. Impedance is not a critical value and designations such as low impedance or high impedance usually suffice. (Impedance is covered in greater detail in Chapter 4).

THE MICROPHONE TRANSFORMER

Still considering Fig. 2-4, we could take the sound signal, now an audio voltage, from across fixed-resistor R, similar to the manner shown earlier in Fig. 2-3. We could feed this voltage into an amplifier and use it to drive a speaker. This supplies us with a problem, however. For maximum transfer of signal the impedance of the microphone should be relatively similar to the input impedance of the amplifier. The carbon microphone, though, is a current-operated device. A rather large current will flow through resistor R in Fig. 2-4. But a large current is synonymous with low impedance, so we look on the carbon microphone as a low impedance device. (Note that we do not supply you with the exact amount of impedance in ohms.)

To be able to get the most signal transferred from the carbon microphone to the input of a following amplifier, we need some sort of interfacing device. This device can be a microphone transformer, as shown in Fig. 2-5. The transformer can be built right into the microphone case or it can be a separate item.

Like other electrical components, the transformer also has impedance, with the impedance depending, to a considerable extent, on the number of turns of wire. The transformer consists of two coils of wire, each wound around an iron core,

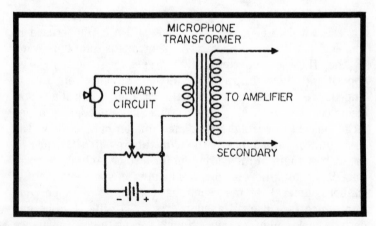

Fig. 2-5. Carbon microphone and microphone transformer.

but with each coil physically independent. One coil, the primary, contains relatively few turns, so its impedance, its opposition to the flow of current, is comparatively small. The other coil, the secondary winding, has many more turns. It has a much higher impedance than the primary winding. This makes the microphone transformer an impedance transformation device. The voltage across the primary winding is small, the current comparatively large. Conversely, the voltage across the secondary winding is larger, the current is smaller. Thus, the transformer in this case is not only an impedance changing device. it also supplies a voltage step-up. The higher impedance of the secondary winding matches the input impedance of the amplifier to which it is connected, not precisely down to the last ohm, but at least both impedances, that of the secondary winding and that of the amplifier input, are somewhat close.

The transformer supplies still one more advantage. While we need the current from the battery to actuate the carbon microphone, we do not want this battery interfering with or supplying any voltage to the amplifier. Because the transformer primary and secondary windings are distinct and separate, there is no way for the voltage of the microphone battery to get over to the secondary winding and, from there, to the amplifier. Thus, the transformer also supplies a needed isolation for the microphone battery.

THE CRYSTAL MICROPHONE

Today we have all sorts of microphones. There are some which make all voices, including those of women, sound as though they consisted chiefly of bass tones. However, you shouldn't downgrade a microphone without first considering its function. A crystal microphone is adequate if you are looking for sound output without any consideration for sound quality. The crystal microphone has a high output. This means you can connect such a microphone to an amplifier without worrying whether or not the output voltage of the microphone will be enough to drive that amplifier satisfactorily. That's why such microphones are popular with manufacturers who are willing to supply you with a mike, amplifier, and speaker at what may seem to be bargain prices. If you want a microphone for fun and games or for partying, and you aren't concerned with sound quality, there's nothing wrong with using a crystal microphone.

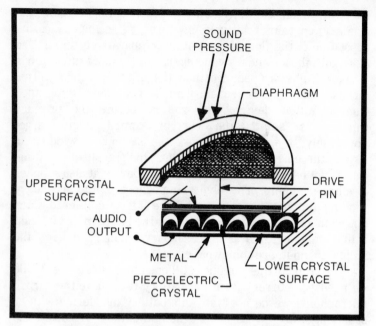

Fig. 2-6. Basic structure of the crystal microphone.

The heart of the microphone is a crystal of *Rochelle salt*. A diaphragm is held in position around its circumference by a metal ring (Fig. 2-6). While it is fixed along its edge, the diaphragm is flexible enough so the area near its center can move back and forth. A drive pin is attached to the center of the diaphragm with the other end of the pin fastened to a metal plate.

Placed near the diaphragm is a metal sandwich consisting of a pair of metal plates, with a filling consisting of the crystalline substance. The bottom plate is fixed in position, but the upper plate, the plate attached to the drive pin, is free to move. With this arrangement, sound waves from your voice or from musical instruments push against the diaphragm, which, in turn, pushes the drive pin, which, in turn, pushes against the top metal plate. The diaphragm is made of spring metal, so the movement of the diaphragm is somewhat in step with the varying pressure produced by the sound.

The crystal material, then, is subjected to a series of varying pressures, depending on whether the diaphragm is moving forward or back, which, or course, depends on what the voice or music pressure is doing at the moment.

PIEZOELECTRIC EFFECT

The crystal material used in the crystal microphone, has an unusual electrical property known as the *piezoelectric effect*. The varying pressure of the metal plate transmitted to the surface of the crystal tends to deform the crystal slightly, permitting the crystal to resume its normal shape when the pressure is removed (Fig. 2-7). This deformation generates an alternating voltage at the rate of sound-pressure change. This microphone, like the carbon type, is basically an alternating voltage generator. Unlike the alternating voltage produced by your local power company, usually a fixed frequency of 60 Hz, the output of the microphone is an entire range of frequencies covering the sound spectrum.

One of the advantages of the crystal microphone is that it supplies a moderately high output-signal voltage for a given sound input. However, the crystal can easily be damaged by high temperatures and high humidity levels. Its frequency response is too poor to make it suitable for recording work, but it is used mostly in voice communications, where the objective is intelligibility of sound.

The output impedance of the crystal microphone is high, so it can be connected to the high input impedance of an amplifier without resorting to a microphone transformer. Still another advantage is that crystal microphones can be made quite small, hence are suitable for applications such as hearing aids.

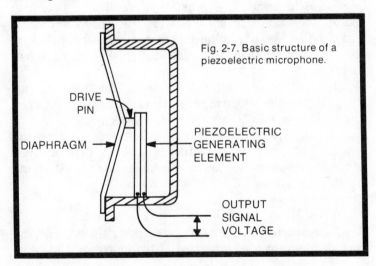

Fig. 2-7. Basic structure of a piezoelectric microphone.

DRIVE PIN

DIAPHRAGM

PIEZOELECTRIC GENERATING ELEMENT

OUTPUT SIGNAL VOLTAGE

Not all crystal microphones use a diaphragm for exerting sound pressure on the crystal element. In some, known as *sound cells*, the air pressure produced by a voice or instruments is applied directly to the face of the crystal. In the sound cell, a pair of crystal elements are mounted in a housing and separated by an air space. Both crystals are subjected to sound pressure and both produce a voltage corresponding to the variations in sound. The voltages are *additive*, so this type design supplies a better frequency response than the diaphragm-driven type. One of the other advantages of the sound cell is that a number of crystals can be used, connected in parallel. This has the effect of lowering the impedance. In areas of high heat and humidity, however, the crystal microphone, no matter how constructed, may declare a holiday and lower its output voltage.

THE CERAMIC MICROPHONE

One way of identifying microphones is through the name of the material used as the transducing element. In the carbon microphone it is carbon, in the crystal microphone it is a substance that has piezoelectric properties, and in the ceramic microphone it is barium titanate. The ceramic mike is a bit better than its crystal counterpart in the heat and humidity departments and it also has a rather high signal output, but it tends to have a frequency response that resembles a roller coaster. What goes in may sound sweet; what comes out may be pickled in brine. It is possible to manufacture ceramic microphones having a smooth, wide frequency response, a response that is fairly uniform. There is a tradeoff, however, and the payment that is exacted is a smaller output signal voltage.

The voltage-generating element in the ceramic microphone has piezoelectric properties; that is, the substance will develop a voltage across its faces when subjected to a pressure and then released (Fig. 2-7). In this respect, then, the ceramic mike is similar to the crystal type. For a given frequency response its output is comparable to that of the crystal microphone.

DYNAMIC MICROPHONES

While both ribbon and moving-coil mikes are dynamic, the word *dynamic* has been applied to the moving-coil mike so often that *dynamic* and *moving coil* have become synonymous. Thus, if you order a dynamic mike, it is extremely likely that you will be supplied with a moving-coil type, not a ribbon. Moving-coil mikes are sturdy, aren't bothered by humidity and temperature changes encountered in the home or studio, and are sensitive.

The Ribbon Microphone

The ribbon microphone, also known as a *velocity* microphone, consists of a thin, stretched duralumin ribbon approximately ¼ inch wide and 2 to 4 inches long, suspended between the poles of a permanent magnet. The ribbon is clamped at both ends but, except for these ends, it is free to move back and forth (Fig. 2-8).

Any metallic conductor moving in a magnetic field will have a voltage induced across it. This is the basic principle on which your local power company's utility generators work. So the ribbon microphone is first cousin to an electric generator with the magnetic field supplied by a magnet shaped somewhat in U form. Attached to the magnet are a pair of pole pieces that saturate easily with the magnetic lines of force supplied by the magnet. These magnetic lines of force extend from one pole piece to the other, and the ribbon is positioned directly in the magnetic field. When the ribbon is made to move it will produce a voltage. This voltage is AC, not DC, and has a frequency corresponding to the frequency of the impinging sound waves.

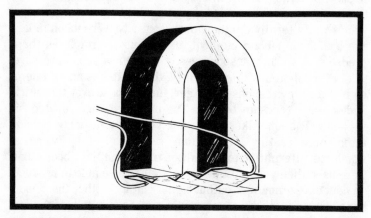

Fig. 2-8. Basic structure (highly simplified) of the ribbon microphone. The ribbon is secured at both ends, but is still free to move.

The ribbon inside the microphone, like all metallic conductors, has a certain amount of opposition to the flow of current. The duralumin ribbon inside the velocity mike is no exception. When measured with an instrument such as an ohmmeter, the DC resistance is about 1 ohm, or possibly less. You can consider this equivalent to the impedance of the microphone and it is extremely low. For this reason, such microphones contain a step-up transformer mounted in the mike case. The step-up transformer actually performs a double function. As in the case of the transformer for the carbon microphone, it is an impedance transforming device, enabling the microphone to be connected to the much higher input impedance of a preamplifier. At the same time, the step-up transformer raises the output voltage. With the transformer, the ribbon mike has a typical impedance of about 200 ohms. While this is a single-value impedance, some ribbon mikes supply a choice of impedances, such as 30, 150, and 250 ohms. In a typical ribbon mike the frequency response extends from 35 Hz to 18 kHz, plus or minus 4 dB. For other ribbon mikes the response may be wider.

The ribbon microphone is sensitive only to sounds coming at it from the front or back, and *not* from the sides, so such microphones supply a bidirectional or figure-8 pickup pattern.

One of the very severe problems of older ribbon microphones was the extreme fragility of the ribbon. The ribbon could be damaged by blowing across it with the mouth in close proximity to the microphone head. Coughing into such a mike was an invitation to disaster. Used outdoors, a strong wind could literally rip the ribbon apart. Newer ribbon mikes use a shorter ribbon element and aren't as fragile as their predecessors. They respond easily to the low sound-pressure level of treble tones. Consequently, this mike has an excellent high-frequency response. Further, the response over the entire audio range tends to be flat. The output voltage, though, is very low. Ribbon mikes were widely used in the early days of radio broadcasting and studio recording. They were a wonderful alternative to the carbon make. But the ribbons that were used then were soft and very light. To be able to produce an adequate amount of output signal voltage, either the ribbon had to be large, or the permanent magnet surrounding it had to be very strong (and this meant very large), or both. But to get good frequency and transient response there was no choice but to make the ribbon small. So the surrounding magnet was made correspondingly larger to supply an even stronger magnetic field. The result was that such microphones were heavy and bulky. In recent years magnet design has enabled manufacturers to reduce magnet size without decreasing magnetic field strength, so you will see some ribbon mikes that have a more practical size.

Few manufacturers are now making ribbon mikes. Those that are available are more rugged than they used to be. In some you can even replace the ribbon. They generally have a smoother response than the much more popular moving-coil mikes. Their treble rolloff is gentle and they do not have much of a popping problem.

The Model M 500 N(C) (Fig. 2-9) is a dynamic hypercardioid ribbon mike by Beyer suited for high sound level applications. Its ribbon measures only 0.85 in. in length and weighs only 0.00034 gram. It contains a four-stage blast filter making possible hand held use with lips almost touching the mike without danger of popping, hissing, or breathing sounds. This mike was developed to cover the special needs of pop vocalists and instrumentalists and is capable of withstanding a sound level of more than 130 dB. The M 500 is unaffected by extremes of atmospheric conditions.

Model M 260 N (C) is a unidirectional ribbon mike with a flat frequency response from 50 Hz to 18 kHz. Unwanted sound is heavily damped, reaching a maximum of 20 dB at 120°. Normally, cardioids provide greatest rejection at 180°. It produces suppression of "off mike" musicians and vocalists in stereo and multi-mike situations. It is also available with a voice-off-music switch supplying a bass cut of 12 dB at 50 Hz, thus allowing close talking without booming or bass accentuation.

The Moving-Coil Microphone

If you know how a loudspeaker works you already know how a moving-coil microphone functions, for both use the same basic principles. You can consider the moving-coil mike as a reverse form of speaker. In intercom systems, for example, the dynamic speaker is also used as a dynamic microphone.

Like a speaker, a moving-coil microphone (Fig. 2-10), now better known as a dynamic microphone, contains a coil consisting of a few turns of wire. This coil of wire is attached to

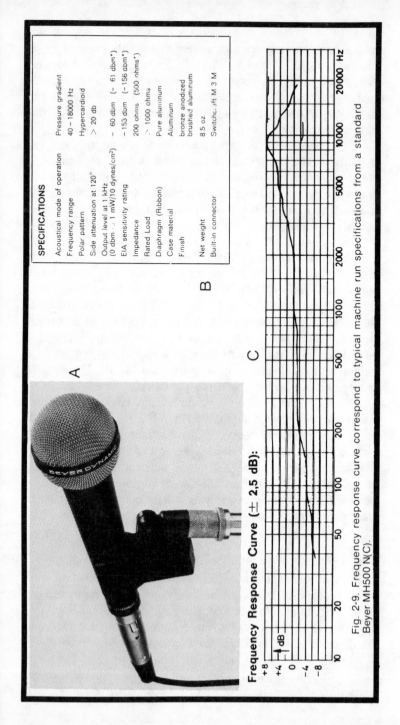

SPECIFICATIONS

Acoustical mode of operation	Pressure gradient
Frequency range	40 – 18000 Hz
Polar pattern	Hypercardioid
Side attenuation at 120°	> 20 db
Output level at 1 kHz (0 dbm = 1 mW/10 dynes/cm²)	– 60 dbm (– 61 dbm*)
EIA sensitivity rating	–153 dbm (–156 dbm*)
Impedance	200 ohms (500 ohms*)
Rated Load	> 1000 ohms
Diaphragm (Ribbon)	Pure aluminum
Case material	Aluminum
Finish	bronze anodized brushed aluminum
Net weight	8.5 oz.
Built-in connector	Switchcraft M 3 M

A

B

C

Frequency Response Curve (± 2,5 dB):

Fig. 2-9. Frequency response curve correspond to typical machine run specifications from a standard Beyer MH500 N(C).

and suspended by a nonmetallic diaphragm, made of a material such as plastic, Lexan, or Mylar. While the diaphragm is supported along its outer circumference, it is free to move easily back and forth. When it does, it moves the small coil of wire. The coil slides back and forth along one arm of a strong magnet. Once again, a conductor moving in a magnetic field will have a voltage induced across it—and that is exactly what happens now. When a sound wave pushes against the diaphragm, it will move it, at the same time moving the attached coil.

In a way, the voice coil is comparable to the ribbon of the ribbon microphone. Both work similarly, for both consist of conductors moving in a magnetic field. The advantage of the coil, though, is its much greater length compared to the ribbon. Actually, we can consider the coil as a ribbon wound in circular form. This greater length results in a much larger induced voltage and, as a consequence, the moving-coil mike develops a much greater output signal voltage for a given sound pressure input than the ribbon mike.

Bass Reflex Techniques

Bass-reflex speaker techniques are sometimes included in dynamic mikes to extend and improve low-frequency response. In a bass reflex speaker, ports or vents are used to allow the back pressure created by the moving cone to be utilized, making such speakers more efficient than acoustic

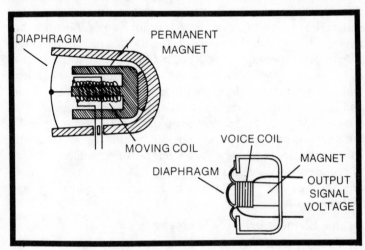

Fig. 2-10. Basic structure of the dynamic (moving-coil) microphone.

suspension types. In other words, in a bass reflex speaker, the air that is normally trapped in the rear of the enclosure is allowed to escape through the front, supplying reinforcement to bass sounds.

In the dynamic mike, the trapped air volume within the microphone body is often used with the mike housing, working as a bass reflex enclosure for extending and improving low-frequency response. Unlike bass reflex speakers, however, the dynamic mike can include a bass attenuation control, so the amount of bass response can be adjusted. This is done mechanically by gradually closing the internal reflex port, using a rotating ring below the head, or electronically with a tone control switch.

While microphones and speakers work at opposite ends of sound systems, they are similar in a number of respects. Like speakers, the mass, dimensions, shape, and efficiency of all moving parts of the mike, plus maximum utilization of the magnetic field supplied by the built-in permanent magnet, are all responsible for total response, low distortion, and accurate translation of the sound input into a corresponding signal voltage at the microphone connector pins.

Advantages of the Dynamic Microphone

Of all microphones available the dynamic or moving-coil types (Fig. 2-11) are the most widely used. They are the most dependable, most rugged, and most reliable design for both indoor and outdoor work. These microphones are capable of the smoothest and most extended frequency response when compared to carbon, crystal, and ceramic types. Because they have a happy combination of highly desirable characteristics—good transient response, a fair to good output signal level, smooth and wide frequency response, high reliability, and moderate cost—they are more widely used in both studio and home recording than any other type of microphone. This does not mean that all dynamic mikes are automatically good. Whether a dynamic mike does have all these desirable characteristics depends entirely on the manufacturer. A good microphone is like a fine watch. It takes a considerable amount of expertise, know-how and responsibility to make one. The same is true of microphones.

Double-Element Dynamic Microphone

The AKG double-element dynamic microphone (also called two-way or coaxial mike) uses a separate high-frequency element, a *tweeter*, coaxially mounted over a separate low-frequency element, a *woofer*. The system crosses over acoustically and electrically at 500 Hz, like a two-way loudspeaker system.

CONDENSER MICROPHONES

A basic condenser (Fig. 2-12) consists of a pair of metal plates separated by an insulating material called the *dielectric*. When you connect a *condenser*, more properly called a *capacitor*, to a voltage source such as a battery, the capacitor will take an electric charge. This means there will be a voltage across the plates of the capacitor. The amount of this voltage will depend on the kind of dielectric used, the area of the plates of the condenser, and how close they are to each other. It is this latter fact that makes the condenser mike possible. If you make one of the condenser plates fixed and the other capable of moving, you can then have a variable voltage device. If you can manage to push one plate closer to the other, the voltage across the condenser will be larger. Conversely, if the moving plate is farther away, the voltage across the condenser becomes smaller (Fig. 2-13).

In the condenser mike we manage to fulfill these conditions. Since one of the plates is able to move, we can use sound pressure to make it do so. In the condenser mike we have a metal-plate diaphragm, tightly stretched but capable of movement. The diaphragm has a very low mass, highly important for the ability to reproduce musical transients. It is often made of some plastic material, such as polyester film, but plastic is a nonconductive material. To make it conductive it is coated with an extremely fine, thin covering of gold. The diaphragm then forms one of the plates of the condenser, and its plastic backing the dielectric. The dielectric faces the fixed-position gold-plated ceramic backplate (Fig. 2-14).

This arrangement supplies a condenser, but by itself it is inadequate. What is now needed is a charging source, a device that will put a voltage across the capacitor. Known as a polarizing voltage, it is a DC potential ranging somewhere between 50 and 200 volts.

With no sound input to the microphone, the *potential*, the polarizing voltage across the condenser element, remains fixed. However, a sound pressure, supplied by voice or musical instrument, will cause the diaphragm to vibrate and,

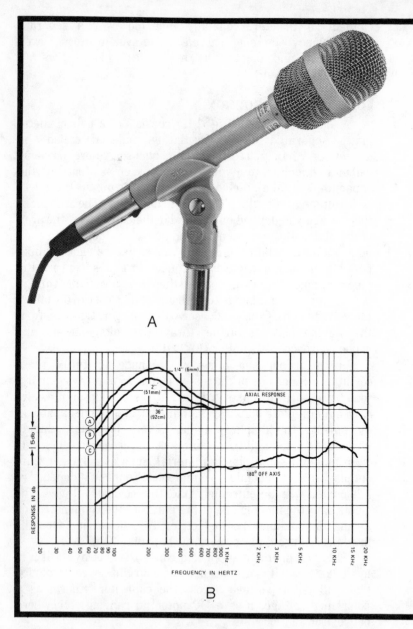

A

B

as it does so, the charging ability of the condenser element will vary accordingly. As the diaphragm moves in toward the back plate, the charge across the condenser will become larger; as it moves away it will become smaller.

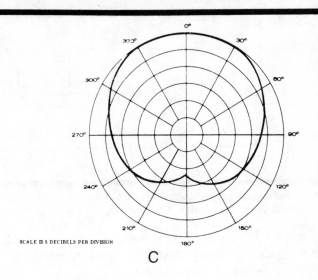

SCALE IS 5 DECIBELS PER DIVISION

C

SPECIFICATIONS

Type:	Dynamic
Frequency Response:	60 to 17,000 Hz
Directional Characteristics:	Cardioid
Impedance:	150
Sensitivity:	−60 dBm
Diaphragm:	Acoustalloy with laminated Volumetric dome
Dimensions:	7¼″ long; 1 7/8″ diameter ¾″ (19mm) shank diameter
Weight:	9 1/5 oz

D

Fig. 2-11. A dynamic microphone. Electro-Voice Model DS35.

Note what we have here. We have a voltage change, but more important is that this change will be in step with the incoming sound pressure level. We can take this voltage change and lead it into an amplifier, either a tube-type or

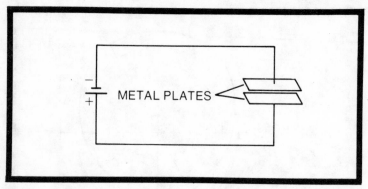

Fig. 2-12. A capacitor (or condenser) consists of two or more metal plates. When connected across a battery, the capacitor will become charged.

solid-state. In either case, we can amplify the voltage change until it is strong enough to supply a corresponding varying current for recording on magnetic tape.

The very small signal voltage developed across the plates of the condenser microphone cannot be used directly. This output voltage could be "wiped out" simply by connecting a

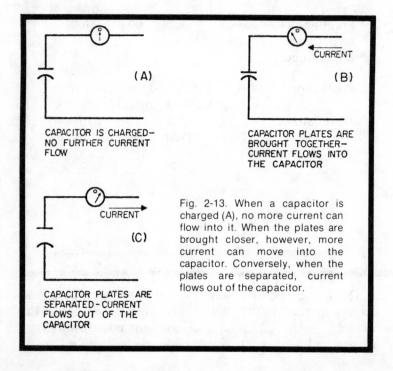

CAPACITOR IS CHARGED—
NO FURTHER CURRENT
FLOW

CAPACITOR PLATES ARE
BROUGHT TOGETHER—
CURRENT FLOWS INTO
THE CAPACITOR

CAPACITOR PLATES ARE
SEPARATED—CURRENT
FLOWS OUT OF THE
CAPACITOR

Fig. 2-13. When a capacitor is charged (A), no more current can flow into it. When the plates are brought closer, however, more current can move into the capacitor. Conversely, when the plates are separated, current flows out of the capacitor.

load, such as an output cable, across the condenser plates. An impedance converter is incorporated directly in the microphone to act as an interface between the required input impedance and the capacitor.

The output impedance of condenser microphones (Fig. 2-15) is extremely high and, to avoid the use of connecting cables, the amplifier is built right into the microphone. Even with miniature tubes, vacuum-tube amplifiers aren't noted for their small size, so early condenser mikes were large and heavy.

When solid-state devices came along, two things became possible. The first was that transistor amplifiers could be

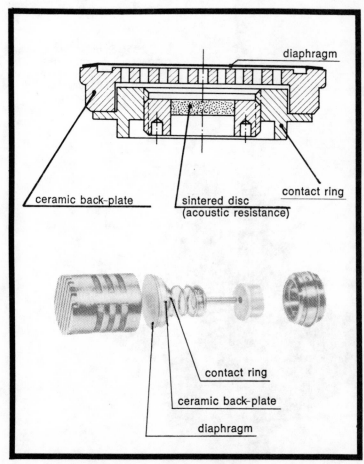

Fig. 2-14. Structure of AKG CK-1 condenser capsule.

Fig. 2-15. Popular professional condenser microphones. The Neumann U-87, top, and the EKG C-414EB with accessory H-17 suspension/windscreen.

highly miniaturized. They occupied a fraction of the space demanded by tubes. Tube amplifiers also required a substantially sized power supply. Transistor amplifiers, though, could work nicely from small batteries. The amplifier and its battery and the battery for supplying the polarizing voltage were all moved directly into the condenser mike housing. Not only do such mikes have excellent frequency response and low distortion, but because the mass of the diaphragm is extremely low, transient response is excellent.

From a technical viewpoint, the so-called "amplifier" in the condenser mike also functions more like an impedance changing device. A transformer is used in the carbon mike to convert the very low impedance of the mike to a somewhat higher impedance through the use of a step-up arrangement. The amplifier in the condenser mike does the same work—but in reverse. It takes the extremely high impedance of the capacitor and converts it to a much lower impedance. Without this impedance converter, the impedance of the condenser mike is in the order of 10,000,000 (10 megohms). At the output of the converter, the impedance is somewhere between 50 and 200 ohms.

Until recently, condenser microphones were very expensive and cumbersome, due to the associated power supply needed. Modern condenser microphones can be powered with batteries, or they can use a "phantom powering system" with power taken from an associated amplifying or recording equipment.

THE ELECTRET MICROPHONE

There is no question that the condenser mike is a superior type, but its structure is complicated by the fact that it does require two voltages—a voltage supply for the self-contained transistor amplifier or impedance converter, and a polarizing voltage for the condenser element.

The *electret* microphone (Fig. 2-16) belongs to the condenser microphone family. The powering requirements of the electret microphone are handled by incorporating a self-polarized or electret capacitor element within the microphone. If you take an ordinary capacitor of good quality and induce a voltage across it, the capacitor will become

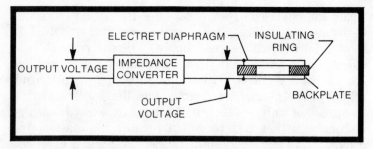

Fig. 2-16. Structure of an electret condenser microphone.

charged. If you then remove the voltage, the capacitor will retain its charge, quite often for a long time. The electret is a specially designed capacitor that will hold a charge indefinitely. This means, then, that the electret can be charged by the manufacturer during the process of constructing the microphone, a step which eliminates the polarizing voltage requirement of the condenser mike.

The impedance converter inside the microphone case, however, still requires its own power supply, but this can be handled by a small penlight type battery.

Chapter 3
Microphone Response

MICROPHONE RESPONSE

Depending on how a microphone is designed and constructed it will have 'areas of sensitivity'. These are the areas in which the microphone will be more or less sensitive to sound pressures. The word 'area', though, could be regarded as technically inaccurate since it implies a two-dimensional surface. The air pressure that reaches microphone elements arrives at the microphone from all directions, above, below and from the sides. This does not mean a microphone will necessarily respond equally to all changes in air pressure produced by the voice and musical instruments. The microphone can be more receptive to sounds arriving from one direction than from another.

POLAR PATTERNS

While the response of a microphone is three-dimensional, and while we could possibly sculpt the response in three-dimensional form using clay or some other medium, such an approach isn't practical. Instead we graph the response in two dimensions by drawing it on a flat sheet of paper.

A *polar diagram* is a type of graph that is particularly suitable for showing the directional response of a microphone. The polar pattern is a way of graphically indicating the sensitivity of a particular microphone to sounds which arrive

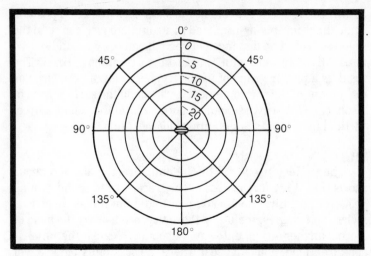

Fig. 3-1. Basic polar diagram. The small elipse at the center is the microphone.

from every possible direction. In its construction, as shown in Fig. 3-1, the diagram initially consists of a series of concentric circles, with the outermost marked 0 dB, the next circle, moving inward, as −5 dB, the next as −10 dB, then −15 dB, and the final circle, the one closest to the centrally pictured microphone, as −20 dB.

Every circle, no matter how large or small, can be equally divided into 360°. In the case of the polar diagram it is regarded as a pair of semicircles, each 180° and joined. Thus, in the polar diagram of Fig. 3-1, we start with 0° at the top and end along a vertical line drawn from that point (at 180°) at the bottom. If we move along the circumference, from the 0° point, either left or right, we will cover a total of 180° each way. At the 90° point a line is drawn horizontally through the center.

By drawing still another diagonal line halfway between 0° and 90°, on both sides of the circle, we finally have the circle divided into 45° segments. It is on this graph that we plot the directional response curve of a microphone.

Zero degrees on the diagram is a position directly in front of the microphone, 90° is a position at either side, while 180° faces the rear of the mike.

Interpreting the Polar Pattern

At the start, a polar pattern is plotted on a polar diagram. such as the one shown in Fig. 3-1. A sound generator, working at a fixed frequency, such as 1 kHz, is kept in a fixed position while the microphone is moved in a complete circle around the sound source. The distance between the mike and sound source is usually 1 meter, with this distance remaining fixed. The result is a plot or graph of the microphone output. The circular movement of the microphone is a trip along the surface area of a sphere. This traverse can be horizontal to the sound source, vertical to it, or any angular displacement in between.

THE OMNI PATTERN

The pattern produced by the omnidirectional microphone shows that it is more or less evenly receptive to sound coming at it from all directions. You will find omni mikes in various styles, and shapes, including those that are held by the hand of the performer or mounted on a boom. Because the omni is non-directional you can use it where the possibility of pickup of extraneous noise, such as audience noise, doesn't exist or is minimum, or if you want to include sound other than 'dry' or direct sound. (Omni patterns are shown on Page 73.)

THE CARDIOID PATTERN

The omni is just one of several possible pickup patterns. Another is the cardioid, so-called because of its heart-shaped appearance. Also known as the unidirectional, the pickup pattern for this mike appears in Fig. 3-2. Technically, the word 'unidirectional' is a misnomer, for the mike can pick up from the sides.

Note that the cardioid does not have the circular response pattern of the omni, but is rather oblate. It is somewhat pushed in at the back. Its sensitivity is less in the rear than in the front. Physically, the cardioid microphone is open so that sound can reach the diaphragm of the mike from both front and rear. The cardioid case has holes or ports at the rear of the mike.

When the head of a cardioid microphone is pointed at the sound source, on-axis sound pressure drives the diaphragm directly. Sound waves arriving off-axis at the sides and rear of the microphone enter specially designed openings in the microphone body and are channeled through often complicated acoustic "plumbing" to the rear of the diaphragm.

As the angle of sound waves reaching the microphone increases from on-axis (0°), to the sides (90°), and to the cable

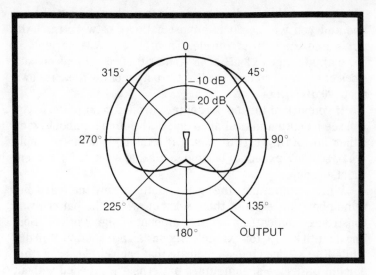

Fig. 3-2. Polar response of a cardioid microphone.

end (180°), sound-pressure differences change between the front and rear of the diaphragm. In a certain sense you can consider the microphone as a kind of computer. It samples the difference in pressure on both sides of the diaphragm and decides which direction of sound reaching it will take precedence. Because of its construction, the cardioid microphone is programmed for maximum sensitivity in the forward direction and gradually reduces its sensitivity to sounds arriving from the sides and rear.

The difficulty with the cardioid polar pattern, as with all other polar patterns, is that (as mentioned earlier) it encourages us to think two-dimensionally. The cardioid pickup is *three* dimensional. Visualize it as a balloon with one side pushed in to make an indentation. The indentation is located at the sound entrances in the microphone body. These sound entrances in the cardioid microphone may be concealed in the head, visible below the head, or slotted on the microphone body. One unusual arrangement is found in an AKG microphone having a two-way double-element system with high-frequency slots around the head and bass-frequency entrances near the connector.

The basic cardioid pickup pattern of a microphone can be pushed, pulled, and squeezed into a variety of modified, three-dimensional shapes, either by design or by accident.

Examine the cardioid polar pattern (Fig. 3-2) at the 90° line and you will see it is almost halfway between the 0 dB circle and the −10 dB circle. Theoretically, the cardioid is down an average of 2 dB at 45° and 6 dB at 90° off axis on both sides of the microphone. At 180° the output of the mike is down about 20 dB or more.

If you look at the top part of the cardioid polar pattern, you will see its output is similar to that of the omni for about 22° on either side of the vertical axis. The total angle in this example is 44°, so don't expect to be able to pick up a single instrument out of a group.

When examining the polar pattern for the cardioid, remember that each of the circles on which the pattern was constructed indicates a relative amount of signal attenuation. The quantity −10, for example, means an attenuation of 10 dB. While Fig. 3-2 does indeed indicate that each circle is a certain amount of decibels, sometimes patterns are supplied without the decibel designation.

Examining the vertical 180° line, you will see its interception is very close to the −20 dB circle. Thus, this particular microphone has an attenuation of somewhat more than 20 dB to signals arriving at it from the rear.

Now consider the 135° diagonal. It intersects the pattern at about the −12 dB point. A signal arriving at the microphone from a position which forms an angle of 135° with the front of the microphone will have this amount of attenuation. According to this pattern, then, you could have signals coming from in front of the microphone to about 22° on either side of the 0° mark. But as you deviate from 22° on either side the microphone becomes less and less responsive to sound.

AXIS OF A MICROPHONE

Figure 3-2 shows the head of the microphone pointing directly to the 0° point on the polar pattern. A vertical line drawn from this 0° point, passing through the center of the head of the microphone, is referred to as its *axis*. Sounds arriving head on, that is, from the 0° point, are referred to as being *on axis*. Sounds arriving at angular deviations from 0° are said to be *off axis*. Thus, sounds that are 90° off axis would be those arriving from 90° and also 270°—the 270° point is 90° from the 0° point.

There is no microphone made that receives sounds only on axis. However, it is the amount of off-axis attenuation that distinguishes one microphone polar pattern from another. Theoretically, at least, a perfect omni would have no signal attenuation at any off-axis point. The cardioid is different than the omni, since it is deliberately designed to have off-axis attenuation.

SOUND REINFORCEMENT

Sound reinforcement consists of a microphone (one or more) supplying a signal to an amplifier which then operates one or more speakers. The amplified sound is an advantage to the performer who can then hear the sound as it is heard by the audience. This enables the vocalist, instrumentalist, or group to make an immediate evaluation of the sound.

In a sound reinforcement system, regenerative coupling of loudspeaker sound into the microphones can cause feedback squeal. Regenerative feedback doesn't necessarily remain constant but can change in amount. Regenerative feedback tends to make sound have a very sharp, edgy quality. As feedback increases, the sound is accompanied by squealing. This obviously calls for some action to be taken to eliminate the cause. Small amounts of regenerative feedback may go undetected since they may not be accompanied by howling or squealing, but it does give the music a ringing quality it should not have.

The reduced directional response of the cardioid to rear sound makes it especially valuable where sound reinforcement is used. Angling the speakers away from the microphones, as in Fig. 3-3, helps to reduce the intensity level of such sound and minimizes the possibility of feedback.

RESPONSE OF THE DOUBLE-
ELEMENT DYNAMIC MICROPHONE

Instead of having a single element, the two-way dynamic microphone has two, with each element designed to favor its respective frequency range. Further, each element can be individually cardioid-tuned to suppress side and rear sounds more uniformly with respect to frequency. The result is a more uniform frequency response at all angles, more uniform suppression of side and rear sounds at all frequencies, and less spitting, popping, or booming when the microphone is used properly. Cardioid response is maintained down to the lowest

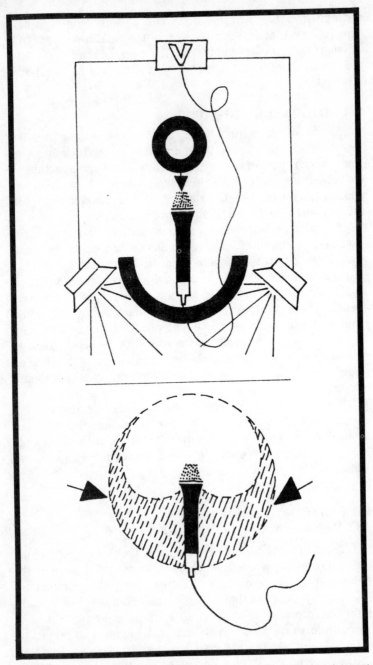

Fig. 3-3. The speakers are positioned so their reproduced sound does not reach the response area of the microphone.

frequencies by slotted openings at the base of the microphone, a longer distance from the low-frequency diaphragm than in most cardioid mikes.

ADVANTAGES OF THE CARDIOID

If you are recording in front of an audience, the cardioid mike will not be responsive to a substantial amount of the rear sound and that includes audience noise. The degree of noise rejection depends on how far the sound is off axis. Compared to an omni, the useful reach of the cardioid pickup extends farther from the mike.

The narrower pickup pattern of the cardioid, though, means you may need to use more of them if you have a number of performers working along a stage. If not, using a single cardioid means that sound from performers near the edges will be weaker in relationship to sounds coming from closer to the center. If these outer edge of the stage performers use instruments whose output is normally weaker in comparison with others, then they will make little overall contribution to the sound.

It is also possible for sound waves to be reflected from the walls of the room used for sound recording. These sound reflections produce reverberation in rooms that aren't acoustically treated and which are normally used for purposes other than recording. Quite often the reverberation is rather strong at lower frequencies.

In the upper drawing of Fig. 3-4 part of the sound leaving the source travels to the left as shown by the straight line arrow, bounces off a wall, strikes the rear wall, bounces once again to an opposite side wall and is then reflected toward the microphone. The reflected wave ends up in the less responsive area. The lower drawing shows that the reverberant sound entering the reduced response area of the cardioid mike is suppressed.

CARDIOID VS OMNI

One advantage of the cardioid is that you can move it further away from the performer, almost twice the distance, before you run into problems of picking up too much reverberant sound or too much background noise or running into feedback from a speaker to the microphone. If, as an example, you use an omni at a distance of 1 foot from the

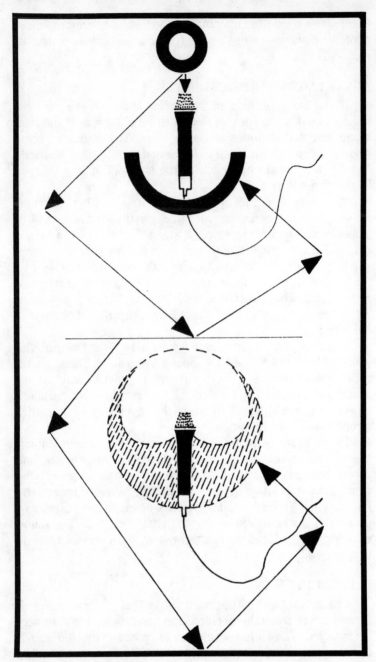

Fig. 3-4. A sound wave may reflect several times from various surfaces. In this example the reflected wave enters the less responsive area of the microphone.

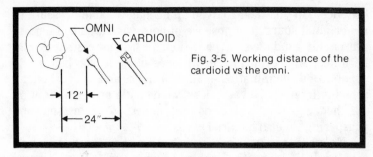

Fig. 3-5. Working distance of the cardioid vs the omni.

performer, you should be able to put the cardioid at a distance of about 2 feet. These are approximate figures and the amount of *working* distance—the distance between performer and microphone—depends on the amount of background noise and how you have your loudspeakers positioned (Fig. 3-5).

For vocalists in sound reinforcement systems the cardioid does seem to be preferable. The performer need not worry about undue pickup of audience noise or the possibility of feedback howling occurring during the performance as compared with an omni.

It is also possible that the loudspeakers may be such a great distance from the microphones that there is no problem of feedback. Under such conditions the omni may be preferable since omnis usually have a smoother frequency response than cardioids. Omnis are less afflicted by popping than cardioids and may be less sensitive to mechanical shock. Sometimes, depending on the manufacturer, it is possible for an omni to be constructed more ruggedly than a cardioid.

SUPERCARDIOID

The supercardioid is somewhat similar to the cardioid in its response pattern. The pattern has two lobes—a front and a rear, with the rear much smaller than the front. Note, also, as shown in Fig. 3-6, the working distance is somewhat greater than cardioid as the shape of the directional response in front is more elliptical. The null regions—regions of little or no pickup— are toward the left and right sides of the mike instead of at 180°.

The directional efficiency of the supercardioid means its reach can be greater than that of the cardioid. One question often asked concerns the extent of microphone reach. The same question could be applied to your ears. Over what distance can you hear? Given an adequate sound pressure of the original source, an absence of noise, and a pair of ears in reasonably good physical condition, the hearing distance could be miles. And even in the presence of noise our hearing is capable of discriminating against the noise and focusing on the sound of interest. Nevertheless, we do put a practical limit on our hearing range. We do not expect to hear someone whispering several hundred yards away.

No more than your ears does a microphone hear all sounds equally well. When the ambient (unwanted) noise becomes disturbingly loud along with the voice or music in a recording, reach is limited. When recording in a quiet studio, distance pickup ends when the system electronic noise becomes apparent in the recording.

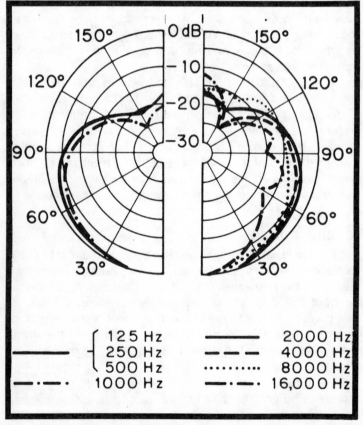

Fig. 3-6. Polar response of a supercardioid microphone.

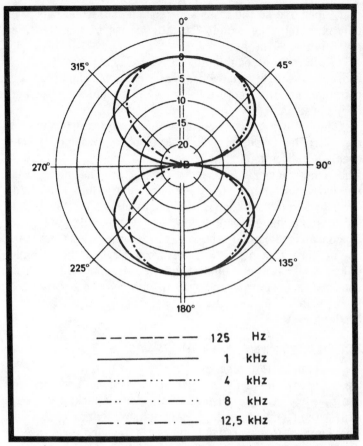

Fig. 3-7. Polar response of a professional bidirectional microphone.

Both the cardioid and the supercardioid are unidirectional microphones with the differences shown by a comparison of the polar patterns for each. Essentially, the supercardioid has narrow segments of response toward the rear while its 90° off axis response is somewhat more attenuated than that of the cardioid. The supercardioid does not work as much against unwanted audience noise pickup as the cardioid. It does not have the rear pickup range of a comparable omni.

BIDIRECTIONAL (FIGURE 8)

The bidirectional microphone response is also called a figure 8 because of its seeming resemblance to that number. As shown in Fig. 3-7, there are approximately equal front and rear lobes and so the front and rear on-axis sound pickup is approximately the same. The attenuation of the signal is maximum at 90° off axis.

A microphone of this kind is very useful when a pair of conversationalists face each other across a table and you want optimum pickup of both talkers and minimum sound pickup from the sides.

The pattern depends on the interior physical structure of the microphone and not upon the type of reproducing element used. A bidirectional mike could be a moving coil type, a ribbon mike, a condenser, and so on. Further, the pattern does not depend on whether the mike is boom mounted, hand held, worn around the neck, or is used in any other way. You could, for example, have a hand-held mike and this mike could be a condenser or dynamic type and its response pattern could be any of those that have been described. Crystal and ceramic mikes are usually available only with an omni pattern. You can have a variety of patterns, though, with mikes that are more suited for high-fidelity use, such as the dynamic, condenser, etc.

POLAR PATTERNS AND FREQUENCY

A polar pattern should be referenced to some particular frequency. While the pattern without a frequency specification can give you an overall idea of the sort of pickup you can expect, the frequency will give you a more definite concept of what happens to directional response as frequency is changed.

Figure 3-8 shows polar diagrams taken at a distance of 1 meter (39.37 inches) from the source of sound. These diagrams are of an omni. The initial frequency is 125 Hz and is represented by the diagram at the upper left. The frequency is shifted in multiples of two—$125 \times 2 = 250$ Hz, $250 \times 2 = 500$ Hz, and so on, until a frequency of 16 kHz is reached. Note how similar the diagrams are to each other. However, the diagram of this microphone at 16 kHz shows a small change in on axis directional response. Other than that, the pickup appears to be quite uniform over the entire range—125 Hz to 16 kHz.

Figure 3-9 shows still another set of polar diagrams, also taken 1 meter from the sound source. These are the patterns of a cardioid microphone. Note that beyond 4 kHz this particular cardioid shows more dramatic change in off-axis response than the omni. This doesn't necessarily mean it is better or

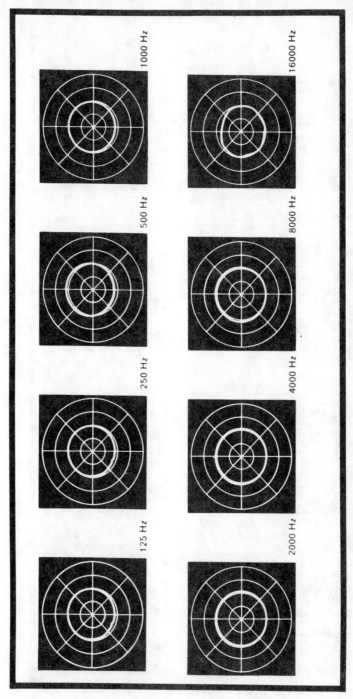

Fig. 3-8. Polar patterns of an omni over a frequency range of 125 Hz to 16 kHz.

73

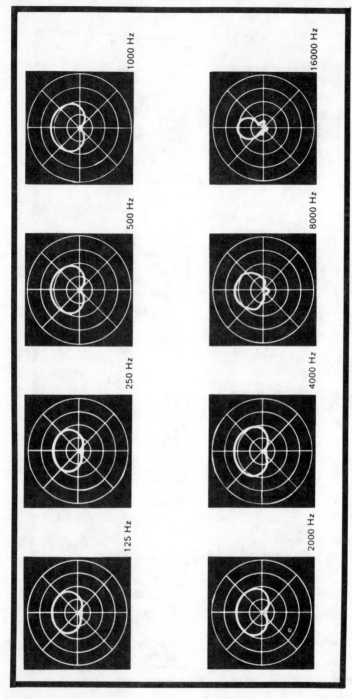

Fig. 3-9. Polar patterns of a cardioid over a frequency range of 125 Hz to 16 kHz.

worse than the omni, just that it is different. It all depends on what you want in the way of a recording.

Figure 3-10 shows the polar patterns of a bidirectional, taken under the same test conditions as the omni and cardioid. This bidirectional also shows changes in directional response over the audio range.

MULTIPLE-FREQUENCY POLAR PATTERNS

While a manufacturer will sometimes supply a total of eight patterns for a particular microphone, more commonly you will see the pattern shown in Fig. 3-11. What you see here is a total of eight patterns all drawn on similar polar graphs. The advantage is that you do not need to examine eight different graphs, looking for significant differences. With the setup in Fig. 3-11, you can see the differences immediately. The problem is that such a graph gets to be quite busy and can be confusing.

PATTERN APPLICATIONS

In practical applications, microphone pickup patterns can be used to help overcome the problems of a less-than-perfect recording environment, while concentrating only on wanted sound. You can use an omni when the possibility of sound feedback and ambient noise is relatively nonexistent. The 360° pickup angle of the omni with relatively equal sensitivity is useful for covering a group of talkers or performers or for recording a conference with the use of fewer microphones. Practically all *lavaliere* body microphones are omnidirectional. Such microphones are normally used close to the sound source and are usually designed to reject resonant frequencies of the chest cavity. Cardioids aren't used in such applications because reflections from the body would play havoc with cardioid characteristics.

While the laveliere microphone is normally suspended from the neck, you can also hang it from ceilings, over choirs for example. Its light weight also makes it desirable when a microphone must be hand held for several hours. Don't make the mistake of equating small physical dimensions with poor quality, however. Despite its small size, a well-designed lavaliere can sound as good as or better than a larger, less well-made omni hand microphone.

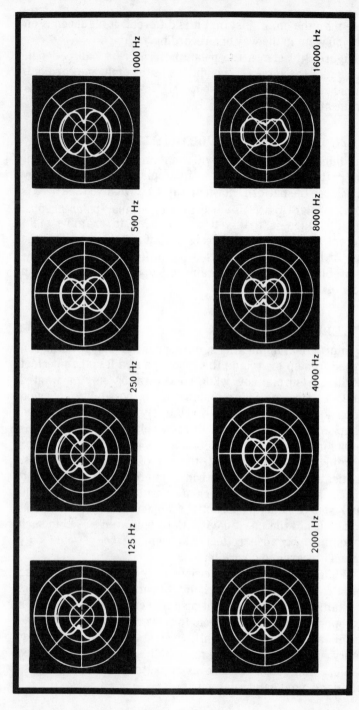

Fig. 3-10. Polar patterns of a bidirectional over a frequency range of 125 Hz to 16 kHz.

1000 Hz

16000 Hz

500 Hz

8000 Hz

250 Hz

4000 Hz

125 Hz

2000 Hz

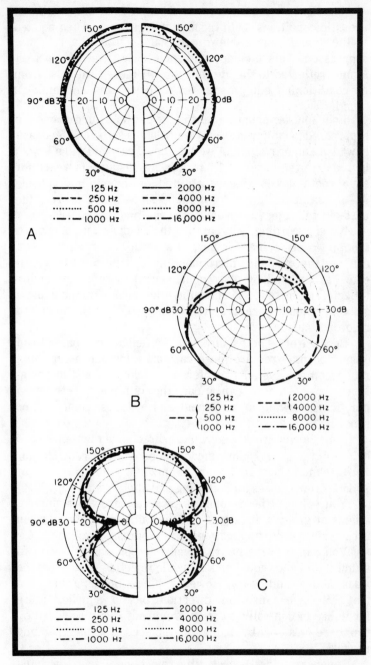

Fig. 3-11. Multifrequency polar patterns for an omni (A); a cardioid (B); and a bidirectional (C).

Cardioid microphones are a distinct advantage in difficult acoustic conditions, both indoors and outdoors. When pointed at the sound source, unwanted sounds from the rear are suppressed. This includes audience noise, live and speaker sounds reflected to the microphone, air-movement noise from air-conditioning equipment, traffic noise, and any ambient sound.

Loudspeaker sounds entering the cardioid microphone are suppressed enabling more system loudness before feedback howl, squeal, or ringing. A well-designed cardioid will allow an increase in the order of 1.7 in working distance or reach for equal room pickup when substituted for an omni microphone. At the same distance from the desired sound source, the cardioid will reject more unwanted side and rear sounds.

When recording, you can use the cardioid microphone to *spotlight* a performer, or part of a group. Alternatively, you can use the cardioid microphone at a distance to cover an entire group, and by placement, permit more or less of the reflected room sound to enter the microphone. By including a suitable amount of reverberant sound you can add warmth to recorded music.

Because of its better directional efficiency compared to an omni, you may require more cardioid microphones in sound reinforcement systems, conference pickups, and recording. However, cardioids can mean the difference between a practical, working arrangement and a useless, marginal or nonoperating system.

In broadcast work, you can use directional microphones to help control studio, announcement booth, and control-room background noises. In TV news applications, the cardioid can subdue crowd noises for reporting and interview pickups.

You can use the cardioid to pick up stage entertainment sounds at greater distances, yet the same microphone, when used in close vocal applications, will suppress stage sounds.

You can position bidirectional microphones between two sound sources for equal pickup, while rejecting sound from the sides, above, and below. However, bidirectionals aren't used that often, because one-direction pickup supplies more flexibility in controlling the environment, easily achieved by two cardioids, or by using one, placed low and pointing upward.

Supercardioids theoretically reject more sound arriving at 150° than at the 180° cable end. In actual practice, the best rejection can fluctuate between the sides and rear with frequency. Supercardioids also have a small pickup lobe at the tail, not evidenced with a pure cardioid. When mounted on a table, desk, or lectern, they will not suppress sound reflected from the close surface any better than a cardioid.

TYPES OF MICROPHONES

You can specify a microphone in a number of ways—by its *polar response*, its *physical structure* (such as dynamic, ribbon, condenser), or by some designation that indicates the way in which it is used. Thus, a microphone can be boom mounted, suspended in some manner, worn around the neck, hand held, positioned in a flexible goose neck, or in a stand. None of these designations describe a microphone totally. Thus, to say that a microphone is supported in a stand tells you nothing of its electrical characteristics. Similarly, to say that a microphone is a condenser-type gives you no information about the way the microphone is to be supported physically.

Some microphones are general-purpose types; others are highly specialized for particular applications.

Shotgun Microphone

Figure 3-12 shows the patterns of the *shotgun* microphone. The shotgun is a highly directional microphone mounted at one end of a long tube. It has reception patterns that vary between modified cardioid shapes at low frequencies to elongated pears at high frequencies, with first a *doughnut* and then a *tear drop* attached to the stem. Rejection of side sounds is much greater than with a standard cardioid. The directional efficiency is even greater than the supercardioid and is narrower. The rear of the pattern sometimes shows a number of small lobes.

Shotgun microphones provide concentrated sound pickup only over a narrow acceptance angle. The microphones are usually a combination of interference tube and cardioid designs for reducing sound pickup from the sides and the rear.

This microphone isn't used in high-fidelity recording unless it is needed to obtain special effects. It finds applications in the broadcasting of sporting events, question and answer microphones at press conferences, and boom use in film and television studios. The directional efficiency varies with the length of microphone tube.

If you will examine the polar patterns in Fig. 3-12 you will see that the shotgun microphone isn't all that directional at

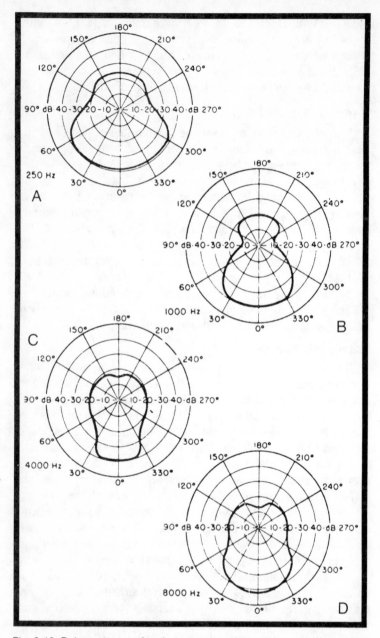

Fig. 3-12. Polar patterns of a shotgun microphone, taken at different frequencies: 250 Hz (A); 1000 Hz (B); 4000 Hz (C); and 8000 Hz (D). Note that the polar patterns have been rotated 180°. The 0° point is at the bottom. Both polar drawing techniques are used, with 0° either at the top, as shown previously, or at the bottom, as shown here.

Fig. 3-13. Lavaliere microphone.

frequencies around 250 Hz (A). It is much better starting around 1000 Hz (B). The patterns also show that the shotgun does have rear pickup, but with front and rear pickup not as evenly distributed as the bidirectional. Useful areas for the shotgun microphone are in a studio where reverberant sound is controlled, or outdoors where it may not exist.

The on-axis sensitivity of a shotgun microphone is not higher in output than a hand microphone with the same type element. The usable degree of pattern off-axis without coloration is simply narrower than cardioids and similar, in addition, to higher directional efficiency.

The higher directional efficiency of a shotgun microphone means, in the end result, that for the same microphone to source distance, the direct signal will be equally loud as a standard directional microphone, but ambient or background noise will be less with the shotgun.

Conversely, for equal ambient or background noise ratio to direct on-axis sound, the shotgun can be farther from the source than a standard directional microphone.

Lavaliere Microphone

The *lavaliere*, shown in Fig. 3-13 and in use in Fig. 3-14, is designed to be suspended from the neck by a string or attached to clothing via a clip or tie tack. The lavaliere has an omni pickup pattern and is most useful when the person wearing it moves around, but it is desirable that the microphone-to-subject distance be kept constant for optimum sound pickup and minimum feedback.

Dynamic lavaliere units can be supplied as standard or shock-mounted units. The shock-mounted units minimize cable and clothing noise but do not supply absolute shockproofing if the microphone is dropped on a hard surface. Electret-condenser lavaliere microphones provide the smallest size. This is useful in film and television applications where the microphone must be inconspicuous.

In case of AKG's Model D-109 lavaliere, a sliding shield boosts the upper-range frequency response. The unit can be freely suspended around the neck or held in position with a tie or clothing clip.

Fig. 3-14. A lavaliere microphone maintains a relatively constant working distance.

Differential or Noise-Cancelling Microphone

The differential or noise cancelling microphone is a special purpose type which works on the principle that if the sound source (a person's mouth) is very close, such as a few inches from the front of the microphone diaphragm, the higher sound pressure level on the front of the diaphragm will produce electrical output while equal pressures on both sides of the diaphragm will cancel output. This type of microphone is most useful for speech communications in noisy environments, such as factories, athletic fields and stores, and recording-studio control rooms.

Stereo Condenser Microphone System

Ordinarily, separate microphones are required for various pickup patterns, such as omni, cardioid, or figure 8. However, a condenser microphone, such as AKG's C-24, contains two twin-diaphragm condenser-microphone capsules mounted within the microphone body permitting *stereo* pickup with a single mike. The spacing is only 1½ inches, making any difference in time between the two outputs negligible. The upper microphone system can be rotated 180° to provide any offset angle desired. Nine different directional patterns can be selected for each of the two twin-diaphragm capsules. These patterns are identical as to their phase relationship and sensitivity and maintain their polar characteristics independent of frequency. The microphone can supply three basic patterns: omni, cardioid, and figure 8, plus six intermediary positions.

The Two-Way Cardioid

The *two-way cardioid* dynamic microphone has a total response range that is divided between a pair of transducers, one for high frequencies and the other for low, analagous to the two-way system used in speakers. In the two-way cardioid, the two systems are connected by a crossover network, with the crossover frequency at 500 Hz. The advantage of this arrangement is a complete absence of proximity effect, a wider flat-frequency response over the entire audible range, and linear off-axis response. This latter characteristic means that sounds reaching the microphone from off axis, such as 90°, are reproduced naturally.

Chapter 4
Microphone Characteristics

MICROPHONE CHARACTERISTICS

To say that a microphone is an *omni*, a *cardioid*, or a *bidirectional* is simply to put it within a general classification. Not all omnis are alike; neither are all cardioids, nor all bidirectionals. Within each group, microphones can have different characteristics.

There are three main design factors used to describe microphones: the *type of transducer* (moving coil, condenser, ribbon, etc); the *pickup pattern* (omni, cardioid, bidirectional); and the *impedance* (low or high). This does not mean these are the *only* mechanical and electrical features, for there are others, such as transient response, frequency response, efficiency, output, and so on.

HOW GOOD MUST A MICROPHONE BE?

All reproduction of sound, whether live or recorded, must begin with one or more microphones. The quality of reproduced sound can be no better than the quality of the microphones used. Consider the microphone as an electronic ear, a substitute for your own. A good-quality tape deck, a superb amplifier, and the best speakers you can buy can do no better than the microphone that precedes these components. It is the microphone that sets the quality level of the performance.

Compared with the cost of all the other components in a system for recording and reproducing sound, microphones are the least expensive. There is a common error made in buying microphones, which is buying solely on the basis of price: either too little or too much. A microphone may be bought at a very low, so-called "bargain" price in an effort to economize somewhere along the line in the purchase of a total system. Or the most expensive microphone may be bought with the thought that the most expensive is automatically the highest quality and will therefore lift the overall quality of a recording system.

There are two criteria in selecting a microphone—*quality* and the *specific use* to which the microphone will be put. There is one guideline to use when buying microphones and that is to buy the best quality, regardless of the kind of sound system you have. If your sound system isn't everything you had hoped it would be, a good-quality microphone will supply reduced distortion and more natural sound reproduction. The microphone will not correct faults in your tape deck, amplifier, or speakers, but at least you can choose a microphone that will not add to your problems. A mediocre system can sometimes be greatly improved by changing the microphone.

Theoretically, the best microphone should cost more, but it is a fallacy to use price as the sole factor in influencing your buying decision. Engineering and manufacturing skills using similar materials do not always produce equivalent results.

MICROPHONE SPECIFICATIONS

Microphone specifications or *specs* are technical descriptions of the way a microphone behaves under certain test conditions. But it does not automatically follow that a microphone which performs well under laboratory examination will sound well. Microphones are tested in *anechoic chambers*—soundproof rooms—but a soundproof room is precisely opposite that of rooms used for recording. Such rooms permit sound to "leak in" from the outside or produce noise from inside, or both. A recording room is a reflective environment in which sound bounces from the walls, floor, and ceiling. Such reflections do not exist in the anechoic chamber where microphone performance is recorded by laboratory test instruments. Your ears are the test instruments when the mikes are finally put to work.

Quite often, microphones do not recreate the sound you hear. This creates a problem because we have been conditioned to expect high quality in reproduction at all times. You expect pictorial quality in the movies you see, you expect it in your television receiver, and the search for sound quality in a high-fidelity system is a constant effort.

BASIC CHARACTERISTICS OF MICROPHONES

You can identify a microphone by considering its physical structure or by its electrical characteristics, but usually the best approach is a combination of both. The heart of the microphone is the *transducer*, the part of the mike that is involved in converting sound energy to its electrical equivalent.

Diaphragm vs Generating Element

In any microphone, a diaphragm is that part which moves in response to sound input, that is, to variations in air pressure presented to the microphone. In turn, the diaphragm moves that part of the microphone which produces the output signal voltage, hence it is known as a *generating element*. In some microphones, the diaphragm and the generating or voltage-producing element are separate components that work together, as in the case of the dynamic (moving coil) microphone. In others, such as the condenser microphone, the diaphragm is an integral part of the generating element.

Any energy conversion, including the conversion of physical sound energy into electrical energy, involves the generation of undesired noise. To keep such noise from being audible, its electrical level compared to the level produced by the useful sound should be as low as possible. This means that at a given acoustic sound pressure, a microphone to be used for high-fidelity purposes should produce as high an electric level as possible.

Microphone Sensitivity

Within the frequency range of any particular microphone, the sound input should create an output voltage that is a direct function of the sound pressure input. A more sensitive microphone would have a larger output signal voltage for a given sound pressure input. Naturally, the farther away the sound source input is from the microphone, the lower the

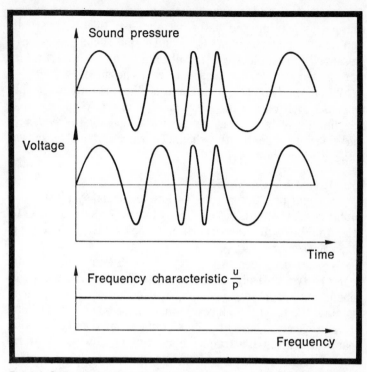

Fig. 4-1. Sound pressure input vs signal voltage output. The lower drawing shows an idealized frequency characteristic.

signal output. *Sensitivity*, then, refers to a signal input of fixed strength at a fixed distance from the microphone. Sensitivity is defined as the voltage or output level of the microphone, in *millivolts*, with the microphone placed within a sound of 1 microbar (a *microbar* is a unit of sound pressure). The measurement is made within a free sound field with the microphone *open-circuited*, that is, not terminated by a load resistor. The ratio of the two—the signal *output* to the sound *input*—is known as either the *response coefficient* or the *sensitivity*.

The sensitivity of a microphone does not refer to a fixed frequency input but, rather, to the entire frequency range specified by the manufacturer of the microphone. If the specs indicate a frequency range of 50 Hz to 15 kHz, the sensitivity refers to this entire range.

The upper illustration in Fig. 4-1 shows a comparison between sound pressure *input* to the microphone and voltage *output*. While the drawings show the sound pressure and output voltage as having the same amplitudes, this isn't at all significant, since sound pressure and output signal voltage are measured in completely different units. What is important is that the two waveforms be as identical as possible.

When plotting the logarithm of the magnitude of the response coefficient over the logarithm of the frequency in a coordinate system, the result is a so-called *frequency characteristic*. Ideally, this should be a straight line, as shown in the lower drawing of Fig. 4-1.

FREQUENCY RESPONSE

You can produce a tone as low as 30 Hz by plucking a double bass. Cymbals have sounds at about 7.5 kHz to above 10 kHz. And the harmonics of certain musical tones go right on up to 15 kHz or more.

What is produced in the way of sound and what you can hear are two entirely different matters. What you can hear depends on your sex, age, physical condition, and musical training. We like to think of human hearing as extending from 20 Hz to 20 kHz. These are outer limits, though, and most of us hear well within that frequency range. Actually, most natural sounds have hardly any low frequencies and quite often what you will find down at the lower end of the frequency scale is noise. This is important, for it establishes a practical set of margins for microphones. A practical response for a microphone could be from 50 Hz to 15,000 Hz, but you will find some microphones that do go down to 20 Hz and some that extend to beyond 20,000 Hz.

A microphone will not only have a specified frequency response, but within its range may prefer certain sound frequencies to others. What we have here now is the possibility that the microphone will alter the sound you pour into it. The variation in frequency response is given in decibels. Such variations range from as little as plus/minus 2 dB to as much as plus/minus 6 dB. A specification of frequency response without an accompanying statement of frequency deviation means you are not getting the whole story about the frequency response of the microphone.

In microphones we can set up a hypothetical ideal which we can then use as a reference standard. *Ideal* is an unfortunate word, for it implies *best*, but ideal is not synonymous with practical. The ideal microphone will have a

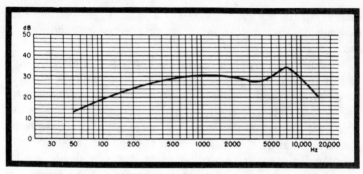

Fig. 4-2. A microphone response curve may have dips and peaks.

flat-frequency response from 20 Hz to 20 kHz, possibly with a deviation of no more than plus/minus 1 dB. There are microphones, such as AKG's C-414 and C-451E, which are as close to this ideal as you can get. But you should not arbitrarily rule against a microphone response which is limited or which has a boost in its midrange, or which is weak at the low- or high-frequency ends. You may find such a response quite useful in eliminating low-frequency problems, in emphasizing voice projection, or if you want to deliberately color sound to produce certain sound effects. Consider also that the frequency response of a microphone can be altered by the way in which it is used. A lavaliere-type microphone when suspended around the neck may produce a certain booming resonance because of its proximity to the human chest cavity. And the same microphone can have a different response when hand held.

As indicated earlier, a microphone is a device for converting sound energy to electrical energy. However, we usually refer to the output of a microphone in terms of *volts*. We put sound in, we get voltage out. If the sound input level remains constant, the output voltage will also remain constant. If we vary the frequency of that sound, the output voltage will still remain constant and will be constant over the entire frequency range. However, the voltage output of the microphone will increase or decrease when its frequency response isn't uniform. This produces the dips and rises or peaks as shown by the curve in Fig. 4-2. The graph indicates that at certain frequencies the microphone is unable to convert a constant sound pressure into equal voltages as the input frequency is varied. Of course, if the input sound level is increased, the output voltage will also increase—or it should. Conversely, when the input sound decreases, the output voltage of the microphone will also decrease.

Frequency response is just as important in microphones as it is in preamps, power amps, tape decks, and speakers. A wide-band, smooth-frequency response always gives cleaner, more distortion-free sound within the range that is actually used (Fig. 4-3). You can equalize—increase or decrease bass, midrange, and treble—to compensate for the acoustic deficiencies of your recording room, but you should not be forced to use equalization to compensate for the frequency response deficiencies of a microphone. That is not the function of equalization.

In some manufacturers' literature, you will find claims made for a microphone having a peaked response as supplying greater brilliance in the treble end, or a peak in the response in the bass as supplying more bass output. There is no point in arguing against microphone response which is limited, stacked in the midrange, misses lows and highs, is peaky, or has dips and rises. As indicated earlier, it is possible to use such characteristics to eliminate low-frequency problems, emphasize voice projection, and deliberately color sound for effect. However, the standard or ideal microphone should have a ruler-flat, wide-range frequency response to sound.

You cannot determine the frequency response of a microphone or its possible response by its physical shape. A pair of mikes may appear absolutely identical in physical appearance, but the fact that they look like twins is no assurance they will have identical frequency responses. And

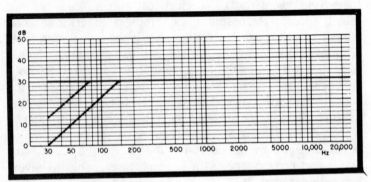

Fig. 4-3. Frequency response curve of a condenser microphone showing two positions of bass attenuation.

this is also applicable to all the other electrical characteristics of microphones as well.

How Low Should Microphone Frequency Response Be?

Preamps and power-amps in modern high-fidelity systems have enormous frequency ranges—20 Hz to 20 kHz is quite common. There are some that go down as low as 5 Hz and beyond 50 kHz. Five hertz is practically DC and 50 kHz is far beyond the upper limits of human hearing.

Shouldn't a quality microphone, then, also go down to 5 Hz? But before microphone engineers work on this problem, isn't it logical for them to ask why? As the frequency response of a microphone is lowered to much less than 50 Hz, it becomes more sensitive to the pickup of hum and rumble. Further, there is very little music information below 50 Hz. And, finally, very few loudspeakers have a clean bass response under 50 Hz. There are very few musical instruments that can go below 50 Hz, such as the bass viol. But this is the very bottom end of the bass viol and such a tone is seldom, if ever, used. *Bottom C* on the piano is around 16 Hz, but this tone is a rarity. The human voice can go down to around 82 Hz, but it takes a trained basso to be able to reach it. Tenors, altos, and sopranos, of course, all start well above 100 Hz.

How Important Is Microphone Frequency Response?

One of the more important characteristics of a preamp, power amp, tape deck, or speaker is frequency response. Amplifiers, for example, can now be manufactured which have responses far beyond the human hearing capability, both at the low- and high-frequency ends. The microphone is the first component in the sound reproduction chain, and if a microphone distorts, or if it does not respond equally well to sound pressures at all frequencies,any modification made by the microphone will be passed along to the next component in the recording setup. The deviation, whatever it may be, will not only be passed along, but will be amplified as well, by the preamp and by the power amp. So the frequency response of a microphone is not only just as important as the frequency response of following components, but more so.

There are microphones which are close to the ideal in frequency response. A good condenser microphone design can be very close to the perfect microphone in all respects, though some condenser types aren't essentially better than excellent dynamics. It is interesting to note that manufacturers making dynamic microphones use only a condenser mike as their laboratory standard reference for measuring their dynamic products. Condenser mikes are the first choice by professional recording, sound-reinforcement, and broadcast engineers for quality sound and maximum suppression of noise, acoustically and electrically.

Which Microphone for You?

From all this it is easy—too easy—to rush to the premature conclusion that the microphones to buy must all be condenser types. However, there are a number of other factors to consider, including the type of use, whether in or outdoors, the musical results you want to achieve, whether in fixed or mobile work, and, of course, the cost. Thus, aside from condenser and double-element dynamic microphones, the single-element dynamic microphone is most capable of extended frequency response and the smoothest performance for quality sound at a reasonable price. Most microphones used today are dynamics.

How Microphones Are Tested for Frequency Response

The frequency response of a microphone is measured in an anechoic room or chamber, a walk-in type enclosure which is carefully lined throughout with highly sound absorbent material. If you were to walk into such a room you would hear any number of sounds normally masked or hidden by noise—sounds such as your heart beat, your breathing, and possibly the sound of your clothing rubbing against your skin. To some the experience is an uncomfortable one, particularly when alone. The presence of others in the chamber contributes some bit of customary, extraneous noise. The entire anechoic chamber arrangement is designed to enable a microphone to hear only the direct sound from a high-quality loudspeaker.

The loudspeaker reproduces sound electrical signals supplied by an audio-frequency signal generator and automatic-gain-control (AGC) amplifier. Mounted next to the microphone being measured is a calibrated condenser microphone. It feeds the loudspeaker signal back to the AGC amplifier, which corrects any variations in loudspeaker output.

The microphone under test is then pointed at the loudspeaker and its frequency response curve is recorded. The microphone is rotated at various angles to the loudspeaker to measure the response at different angles, from direct (0°) to side (90°) and rear (180°). Sometimes angles in between are also recorded. The voltage output in proportion to the frequency and angle of reception are shown as polar patterns. However, these are nothing more than a two-dimensional slice taken out of the three-dimensional pickup pattern surrounding the microphone.

The voltage output of the microphone will increase or decrease when its frequency response isn't uniform. This results in the dips and peaks revealed by the curves, indicating the ability of the microphone to convert sound pressures into equal variations in voltage output.

The off-axis angle measurements also indicate how well a directional microphone suppresses side and rear sound, since these angles should produce less voltage. The angle measurements will be lower on the polar graph, since output reduces with direction. The spacing of the rear measurement below the direct-to-head curve is measured in decibels. This becomes the front-to-back specification of a cardioid microphone.

Rear rejection of sound by a cardioid isn't uniform with frequency and varies all over the entire range. When the microphone tail is pointed at the loudspeaker test source, sound waves must pass over the microphone body to reach the diaphragm. This creates a turbulence, like water passing around a rock, and disturbs the sound field, producing additional variations in sound pressure at the diaphragm. This is why the rear response of a cardioid looks uneven compared to front response.

Cardioid front-to-back ratios in decibels are meaningless for comparison unless the frequency of measurement is specified. Many cardioid designs achieve maximum suppression of rear sounds up to 25 dB weaker at 1000 Hz, but may only suppress rear sounds 2 dB at 8000 Hz. This is a state-of-the-art problem, and final performance of the microphone is best judged under actual-use conditions.

It is also entirely possible that a cardioid with a larger front-to-back ratio number will not work as well as a cardioid with a smaller ratio, since unformity of suppression is more important than maximum suppression at any one frequency.

The frequency response of a microphone is plotted in *decibels* (dB). The decibel scale is a logarithmic scale for measuring acoustic quantities, such as sound level, microphone output, etc. It is related to the physiology of hearing. The sensing device of the human ear is sensitive to low-level sound and much less sensitive to high-level sounds.

A slight rise at the higher frequencies is referred to as *presence rise*. This is desirable at times to add "brilliance" to recordings made in acoustically dull surroundings. Furthermore, presence rise is desirable when recording over a distance so as to capture the quicker decaying high-frequency sound waves.

THE MICROPHONE AT WORK

As a microphone is moved from the anechoic chamber to an open field outdoors, to an outdoor stage, or into a closed auditorium or room environment, it progressively sits in a reverberent envelope of direct and indirect sound. No microphone has a completely dead side. Sound reaching the microphone may be suppressed from the side and rear, but it still generates audible sound, however weak.

The sound reaching a microphone is not only that which is directly in front of the microphone. It is a combination of direct sound from a speaker, vocalist, or instruments, plus reflected sounds from the same source, entering the microphone after it bounces off the walls, floor, ceiling, chairs, people, and possibly even a lectern. All surfaces of all things reflect sound, comparable to the light reflected by various objects. The amount of sound reflection will vary depending on how smooth (hard surfaces) or how soft (rough, textured, or material covered) the surfaces are. The human skin reflects sound and does so much better than cloth. And strange as it may seem, there will be more sound reflection in an auditorium filled with women wearing miniskirts than in that same auditorium occupied by men and women wearing pants. Microphone pickup also includes direct sound from voices and instruments which are located to the sides of the microphone.

THE CONCEPT OF FREQUENCY RESPONSE

A common misconception about frequency response is that the response should be uniform for wanted sound only. Thus, there is an idea that a cardioid need be uniformly frequency-responsive only to sounds within its plotted response pattern. Not so. The ideal microphone should also have a flat, wide-range frequency response to sound arriving from any direction, including sounds which it is suppressing and which are weaker than the direct pickup. The microphone must have this overall-sound flat-frequency response if the total sound is to be natural and acceptable.

But what if the microphone frequency response isn't identical for sounds reaching it from all directions? As talkers move off axis, their voices will change quality. Identical instruments on and off axis will not sound the same. The overall result will be that the total sound is "colored", the side-sound pickup will be dull, and the effect will be that the total sound will seem unnatural.

ON-AXIS VS OFF-AXIS RESPONSE

While a polar response pattern does supply some information about microphone response, it is two dimensional, as discussed earlier. However, the polar response as shown in the graph is but a single continuous line on the surface of a spherical type of three-dimensional object, such as a ball or an apple. To get a truer picture we should examine a large number of polar responses, each forming a sort of circle around the centrally located microphone. Further, we should do this for the entire frequency range of the microphone, selecting spot frequencies. However, such an approach is quite impractical.

In simple fact, the single-element dynamic microphone does not have the same frequency response at all angles. It is generally the frequency response measured on axis. However, an examination of the single, on-axis response curve is a clue, since generally the smoothest curve will give better results on side pickup. Response losses off axis are caused by the microphone getting in its own way and the size of the diaphragm in relation to frequency, which creates a narrower pickup pattern at high frequencies.

Uniform high-frequency response at 90° to the side of the microphone can begin to deteriorate above 1000 Hz and is never good beyond 5000 to 6000 Hz in the best single-element cardioids. Good high-frequency response at side pickup to 90° will generally preserve voice character. Instruments with response and harmonics above 5000 Hz will sound dull and colored when out of line with direct pickup. However, with the double-element type dynamic microphone, sound reaching the microphone 90° off-axis is reproduced naturally.

HOW TO MAKE YOUR OWN CARDIOID RESPONSE TEST

You can make your own evaluation of the off-axis response of a microphone. Speak, sing, or play an instrument with the microphone pointed at the source. Position the microphone at a distance of one to two feet. Set the recording level of your tape deck and record. As a voice test, keep repeating the number 7, selected since it contains both low and high frequencies. Of course, you can also speak, sing, or play an instrument.

Now rotate the microphone off axis. Maintain the same distance from the microphone and use the same sound source you did originally. You will need to raise the recording level to the same volume previously indicated in the first test. This will compensate for the drop in level, up to about 6 dB, due to cardioid suppression at 90° pickup. Now record again.

Rotate the microphone again and point the cable end at the sound source. Remember to keep the same distance from the sound source to the microphone. Raise the volume level once more to compensate for the up to 20 dB average drop in level from cardioid rear rejection of sound. Record again.

If you've done this experiment correctly, the playback level from the three microphone angles should sound equally loud. You will hear the character of sound change with each microphone angle. The microphone which maintains basically the same sound quality over the widest off-axis angle is the better microphone, regardless of price.

You can also make yourself more conscious of possible changes in sound quality when attending a reinforced public sound stage or performing arts stage installation. Close your eyes and listen carefully as the speaker, vocalist, or instrumentalist moves to the left or right of the microphone. With a little practice you will soon begin to note changes in sound quality.

PROXIMITY EFFECT

Except in the case of omnidirectional microphones, the frequency response of a microphone can become distorted when it is used too close to the mouth. The result of such microphone positioning is rasping, spitting, popping, booming, or exaggeration of the low frequencies.

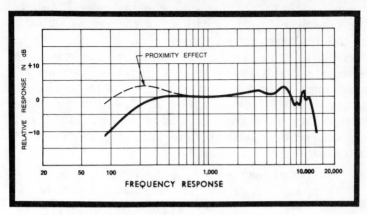

Fig. 4-4. Proximity effect increases bass output.

The mouth is a rather unusual sound source, for it generates spherical sound waves with very high impact pressures. However, as the distance from the mouth to the mike increases, the spherical sound waves tend to flatten, becoming plane waves, so distortion diminishes with distance. You can hear a comparable distortion effect when someone talks or sings within an inch of your ear.

Known as *proximity effect*, it is the increase in low-frequency response produced in most cardioid and bidirectional microphones when the distance from the sound source is decreased, with the effect most noticeable at a distance of less than two feet (Fig. 4-4). Proximity effect can easily introduce up to 16 dB bass boost when the microphone is positioned about one inch from the mouth. Depending on the design and low-frequency efficiency of the microphone, the voltage output can jump many times the catalog sensitivity rating. As an example, a microphone catalog rated at −55 dB can put out a signal of −19 dB.

Cause of Proximity Effect

Proximity effect is due to microphone design. For certain applications some quality microphones are intentionally designed to provide proximity effect. In the simplest and, usually, the least expensive cardioid mikes, the rear sound entrances for side and rear sound cancellation are close to the diaphragm. Because these rear sound entrances are near the diaphragm, the result is an exaggerated, boomy bass boost in voice—an effect that becomes more noticeable as the working distance of the microphone is reduced from about two feet to where the mouth practically touches the mike. Proximity effect is a byproduct of low-cost design, and you will not find it in the response curves shown in microphone catalogs. Microphones with rear sound entrances on the body more remote from the head have less proximity bass boost and will sound more natural when close-talked. The most objective natural sound is achieved when the low-frequency sound entrances are as far from the head as possible. Omnis aren't subject to proximity effect because sound pressures cannot act on the rear of the diaphragm.

How Proximity Effect Is Minimized by Design

Microphone designers are continually working on techniques to minimize proximity effect for those uses where increased bass at short working distances isn't wanted. One technique is the inclusion of a variable distance slot in the handle of the microphone. A tapered length of absorbent material is mounted inside the microphone handle directly beneath the slot, providing variable frequency absorption, depending on the thickness of the absorbent material. The thickest part is placed farthest away from the microphone diaphragm, so high frequencies have the shortest path to the diaphragm, low frequencies the longest path. This provides a more uniform cardioid pattern at all frequencies and minimizes proximity effect. A proximity effect of 4 dB at a distance of 2 inches at 100 Hz has been measured on microphones of this design.

There is a disadvantage, though. A performer can place a hand over part or all of the variable distance slot during a performance. This creates a double-humped peak in mid-frequency response and an increase in proximity effect, depending on the amount of the slot which is covered.

Another proximity-effect reduction has been developed by AKG based on the *two-way* or *coaxial* microphone, described earlier. Proximity effect is reduced because the high-frequency element of the microphone prevents the performer's mouth from getting up to the low-frequency diaphragm. The measured proximity effect of the two-way microphone is 2 dB at 2 inches at 100 Hz, an improvement over the variable-distance slot technique. A side effect of the two-way microphone system is that a midrange proximity effect is produced at 500 Hz, but this is limited to a 1.5 dB rise at a distance of ½ inch from the source. This is well within the response specifications of the microphone.

Utilization of Proximity Effect

You cannot characterize proximity effect by calling it either good or bad. For every microphone user who doesn't want it, there will be another who will depend on it. The best technique is to be aware of proximity effect—how to avoid it if that is what you want, and how to use it if that is what you want.

The most pronounced area in the sound spectrum for proximity effect is below 100 Hz. If the microphone has an extended bass response, such as a condenser mike, low-frequency boost will increase as the frequency is lowered. In hand-held microphones where the low-frequency response below 150 Hz is attenuated to minimize handling noise, proximity effect will produce a noticeable hump around 100 Hz.

There are applications where a low-frequency boost may be desirable. Announcers and vocalists, for example, may want to add fullness to the voice. Vocalists often like proximity effect because the increased bass energy produces a high signal to ambient noise ratio. This supplies the vocalist with greater isolation from accompanying instruments, supplying greater vocal penetration to rock groups and lessened acoustic feedback in some applications.

Proximity effect can also be troublesome. Thus, for a radio announcer who must move around to cue records, start various machines, or is in a situation where the distance from the microphone is constantly changing, proximity effect can cause the announcer's *on-the-air* voice to change character as he moves about. In this application it is better to select a microphone having minimum proximity effect.

Solo performers who are aware of proximity effect sometimes use it to produce a desired result. The performer may work the microphone close anyway, and not only does he keep stage sounds out of the mike, but the voice gets a deeper bass. The sound isn't "natural", it isn't high-fidelity, but the increased bass and exclusion of competing instruments is what the performer wants.

Proximity effect doesn't help public speakers. The exaggerated low-frequency boost produces echoes in the auditorium or hall and these destroy intelligibility. It makes no difference whether the microphone is hand held or mounted. The public speaker isn't able to maintain a constant distance to the microphone. There are sound dropouts whenever the speaker moves left, right, or backward. In some cases the result is that the speaker ends up hunching closer to the microphone. In this example, proximity effect can destroy the effectiveness of the speaker. The use of an operator to control sound-signal gain is no solution, for there is no way in which the operator can compensate for changes in the working distance between the lips and the microphone.

No other single microphone design has set the sound taste of the public or standards for microphone and user performance than the close-ported, single-element cardioid. Properly used, it is versatile. Performers can generate an effect that helps thin voices. The proximity cardioid will reach over distance in public sound and recording when the talker cannot get close to the mike. Improperly used, proximity effect is the greatest offender in obtaining unacceptable sound.

Microphones having a proximity effect characteristic have conditioned users of such microphones to expect close-talking bass boost, and the effect generated is mistakenly assumed to represent a standard for good performance. The effect can be tolerated with a performer or announcer whose thin voice needs enhancement. In sound-reinforcement systems, however, the bass-boost proximity effect is unnatural, and sound equalizers are used to cut its effects. Some microphones do have restricted low-frequency response to compensate for proximity bass boost, but such microphones produce thin sound in normal working-distance applications.

TRANSIENT RESPONSE

Like so many other things, musical notes have a beginning, followed by a sustained portion, and then an end as described earlier, in Chapter 1. If you were to listen to just the sustained part and not hear the beginning, you would probably have difficulty in distinguishing one musical instrument from another. If, for example, a violin and flute both played the same tones and you were not given an opportunity to hear the beginning of these tones, you might not be absolutely certain which instrument was the violin and which was the flute. If you could hear the beginning and the ending of the tones, instrument recognition would be much easier and more definite.

102

However, the beginning or ending of a tone has a much shorter time duration than the sustained portion. The tone starts at *zero* sound pressure level and reaches its peak value quickly. This is similar to the conclusion of a tone. It drops from some high sound pressure level to zero rapidly. These sudden starts and stops of a tone are called *transients*, possibly because they are so fleeting. This does not mean that every tone must have a sustained portion. You could have a transient consisting of a sudden start and an equally sudden finish, with no sustained section. It is these transients that give each tone its personality, its particular characteristic.

The transient nature of tones makes matters a bit difficult for microphones. When a sound pressure level rises almost instantaneously from zero to some peak, it means that the diaphragm of the microphone must move equally rapidly. While molecules of air are extremely light and can rearrange themselves into regions of compression and rarefaction without difficulty, the microphone diaphragm with its much larger mass is more difficult to get into motion and is equally more difficult to stop.

Not all instruments, of course, have tones which have sudden starts and stops. But the percussives do. The piano is a notable example and the ability of a microphone to reproduce the tones of a piano is a good test of the transient response of that microphone.

From a microphone design standpoint, this means that the diaphragm in the mike—the element that responds to changes in sound pressure level—must be lightweight because it must be able to get into motion as quickly as possible and because it must equally be able to stop quickly. One way of reducing the weight of the diaphragm is to make it smaller. And the trend over the years has been toward microphones whose size has been coming down. But if you reduce the size of the diaphragm and of the moving coil, the output voltage of the microphone decreases. Also, a microphone, like a speaker, is contained within an enclosure, and enclosures have *physical resonance* problems. This means they tend to boost sound for certain favored frequencies.

EFFICIENCY

Some speakers, such as the acoustic suspension types, have a very low *efficiency*, which means they require a much higher audio power input to produce speaker sound, and so such speakers are associated with higher-powered amplifiers. A much more efficient speaker can produce the same amount of sound output with a smaller amount of audio power input.

However, microphones do not have the advantage of being able to use power amplifiers. They must always work directly with the original sound source. Further, the signal-voltage generating element in the microphone must always be small and so microphones always develop weak output signals. These output signals are always in competition with noise, and anything that can be done to improve microphone output is always a step in favor of a better signal-to-noise ratio. With a high signal-voltage output microphone, residual amplifier noise and tape hiss are reduced in proportion to the loudness of reinforced voice or recorded music.

There is still another advantage of using a microphone with a high output. The high-output microphone can be used at a greater distance from the sound source before the noise level produced by the system becomes intrusive. But high microphone output is just one consideration among many. Other wanted microphone characteristics may be such as to override the desire for high output.

OUTPUT LEVEL

Microphone *output level*, the *sensitivity* of a microphone, is an important specification. It is the amount of voltage generated by sound pressure driving the microphone diaphragm. Various standards are used, but all relate to a specific loudness with the microphone pointed, on axis, at the sound source, generally at a test frequency of 1000 Hz.

The applied sound pressure is based on practical use conditions. This is the 74 dB to 80 dB average loudness of a speaking voice 3 feet from the microphone, or the approximately 94 dB sound pressure of a speaker 1 foot from the microphone. Both measurements are related because microphone output voltage will double and increase 6 dB as the distance to the sound source is halved. The voltage will drop to one half, or 6 dB, as microphone distance is doubled.

THE BAR

The *bar* is the basic unit of atmospheric pressure, and is 14.7 pounds per square inch at sea level. This is the pressure of the air that rests on us. We exert an air pressure on a microphone diaphragm when we direct sound at it. The sound pressure we put on a microphone, though, is much smaller than atmospheric pressure, actually in millionths of *one atmosphere*. We use the term *microbar*, with the prefix *micro* meaning millionth. If you were to take 14.7 pounds per square inch and divide it by 1,000,000, you would get the amount of pressure put on a microphone diaphragm when we talk into it with a pressure of 1 microbar. The threshold of hearing, the point at which sound first becomes perceptible, is equivalent to 0.0002 microbar.

SOUND PRESSURE LEVEL

Sound pressure level (abbreviated SPL) is measured in decibels. It is an alternative form to the microbar of sound pressure measurement. The threshold of hearing is 0 dB SPL, corresponding also to 0.0002 microbar.

SPL is sometimes preferred as a unit of measurement in place of the microbar, since SPL is in decibels. Decibel ratios, like percentages, are convenient to use. Sound pressure levels, microphone, amplifier, and speaker frequency response curves, system gain, tone control, and similar audio functions are frequently measured in decibels. As a unit of measurement, SPL offers a convenient starting point for sound systems in which all measurements are in decibels.

What is not generally realized is that it requires just an extremely small change in normal air pressure to produce sound. Sound that is barely audible is caused by an increase or decrease in normal air pressure of about one-millionth of one percent. A variation of normal air pressure of about one-tenth of one percent puts sound at the threshold of pain.

THE DECIBEL

The *decibel* (abbreviated dB) is a *ratio*, a comparison of two voltages, two currents, or two electrical powers. It is also convenient as a relative measure of sound level, or sound-pressure level (SPL). The chart in Fig. 4-5 is a scale that supplies a comparison of the relative levels of familiar sounds.

Unlike other units of measurement, such as the inch, the yard, or the meter, the decibel isn't linear. Instead, changes on a decibel scale occur logarithmically. For example, one sound

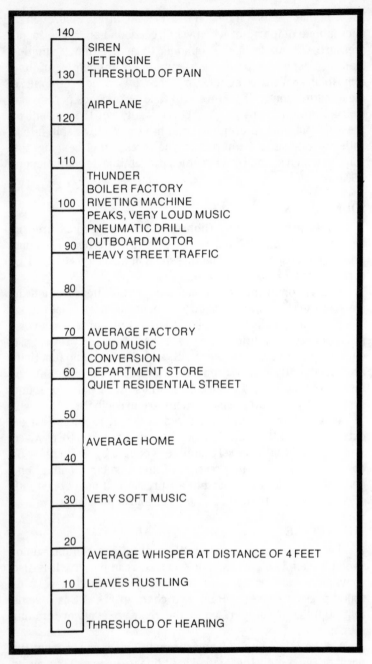

Fig. 4-5. Relative sound levels of ordinary sounds, in decibels. At the threshold of hearing (0 dB), we are barely able to hear the sound.

which is twice as strong as another sound has a level 3 dB higher. And a sound 100 times the level of another is 20 dB higher.

The smallest change in sound intensity that you could notice is about 1 dB. The pressure level of sound produced by an orchestra, its dynamic range of sound from the softest to the loudest, is about 90 dB. Ninety decibels, though, is a ratio of 1,000,000,000 to 1, so when an orchestra is going full blast, the SPL it produces is 1,000,000,000 times greater than its softest passages. Rock orchestras, particularly when using instrument amplifiers, can reach this dynamic range. The microphone must be capable of producing an electrical signal output which corresponds faithfully to this tremendous range of sound pressures.

REFERENCE LEVELS

A measurement is always a comparison, or a ratio. If you make a measurement with a ruler, the comparison is the distance between the left edge of the ruler and the point at which you stop on the ruler scale. The left edge of the ruler is a *reference*. The location of your house is always with reference to some corner.

A *reference* can be any number or starting point you wish. It can be 0, 5, 10, or 1,000,000. The left edge of a ruler is *zero*, and while it is a convenient reference, you could use 1 inch, 3 inches, 6 inches, or any other number on the ruler as your *starting point* or *reference*. When you walk a mile, the point at which you start is your reference, even though it may be a hundred miles from some other point.

Microphone output voltage is usually referenced to 1 volt and power output to 1 milliwatt. Note that a reference can be larger than the voltage or power supplied by a microphone. Thus, a microphone can have an output voltage which is a small fraction of 1 volt. Both voltage and power output of microphones are most often expressed in decibel ratios.

When the measured microphone output voltage is equal to the reference, either 1 volt or 1 milliwatt, we have a one-to-one ratio. Written as 1:1, it is designated as 0 dB. However, since low-impedance microphones generate a weaker signal than the reference, decibel output ratings become negative numbers, such as −50 dB, −55 dB, or −60 dB etc. The minus sign as used here does *not* indicate subtraction. Instead, it is just an indication of how much weaker the output signal of the microphone is compared to the reference voltage or power.

Using SPL is a convenient way in which to compare the sensitivities of microphones. The microphone with the largest negative number is lowest in output. A microphone rated at −60 dB has less output signal than one rated at −50 dB. Conversely, a −50 dB microphone generates more output voltage than one that is specified at −60 dB.

THE DYNE

The microbar and SPL are two different ways of describing the same thing—the pressure exerted on a microphone diaphragm. There is still another, known as the *dyne*, which is also a unit of force. The *dyne* is that force which will produce a velocity of 1 centimeter per second when acting on a mass of 1 gram. In other words, if you had an object that had a mass of 1 gram and if you were to push it so it moved 1 centimeter per second, you would be exerting a force of 1 dyne.

The dyne per square centimeter, written as dyne/cm^2 is equivalent to 1 microbar or 74 dB SPL—10 dynes/cm^2 is equivalent to 10 microbars or 94 dB SPL.

The output voltage of a microphone, then, can be given in millivolts or negative decibels less than a 0 dB reference (abbreviated re) of 1 volt or 1 milliwatt. The microbar is equivalent to the dyne/cm^2. Thus, a manufacturer might supply the sensitivity of a microphone as:

$$-74 \text{ dB re } 1V/\mu\text{bar}$$

Translated, this means that the microphone has an output of 74 dB SPL or 1 microbar. The reference is 1 volt.

Another microphone might be specified as:

$$-56 \text{ dB re } 1 \text{ mW}/10 \text{ dynes/cm}^2$$

The output of this microphone is −56 dB, equivalent to 10 dynes/cm^2 with a reference of 1 milliwatt. The output is 1 milliwatt per 10 microbars.

The disadvantage of having a number of different ways to indicate microphone sensitivity is that it becomes extremely difficult to make comparisons among microphones. As an example, consider this listing:

(1) −74 dB re 1 V/$u$bar
(2) −58 dB re 1 mW/10 $u$bar
(3) −58 dB re 1 mW/10 dynes/cm^2

where

>Item 1 is −74 dB referenced to 1 volt per microbar,
>
>Item 2 is −58 dB referenced to 1 milliwatt per 10 microbars, and
>
>Item 3 is −58 dB referenced to 1 milliwatt per 10 dynes per centimeter squared.

But all of these microphones have an identical output. The use of a higher reference level makes one microphone appear to have more output than another, as in a comparison of item 1 with 2 or 3. An examination of these negative decibel numbers will make one microphone appear more sensitive than another when, as a matter of fact, the voltage outputs of the microphones are just about the same.

Further, the microphone output level is meaningless unless the reference level is given along with the sound pressure loudness, the impedance, and the frequency response. To do otherwise would be like comparing the engine performance of two cars on the basis of gas-mileage only.

QUALITY OF A MICROPHONE

The quality of a microphone isn't normally related to either high or low output voltage. If a microphone has a larger magnet it will generate more voltage, but that is only part of the whole story. Is the output linear? Undistorted? Usually, however, a more efficient use of materials does produce a higher output regardless of comparable element size.

High-output microphones are desirable for reasons of "reach" and a good signal-level-to-noise ratio. If the microphone output is too high for close-in use or loud signal pickup with highly sensitive amplifier inputs, the problem can be solved by using voltage reducing pads. High microphone output levels can be accommodated for optimum results. It cannot be restored when it isn't there at the start. In other words if it has high signal output, you can reduce that output if you need to do so.

MICROPHONE OVERLOAD

Commonly, *distortion* in a sound reinforcement system and during recording is blamed on the microphone. Someone talking directly into a mike at practically lip level can produce up to 100 dB sound pressure level. Loudness impacts on the microphone diaphragm located just a few inches from a screaming vocalist or a loud or amplified musical instrument may reach an average sound pressure level of 120 dB, possibly rising to 130 dB on sound peaks. A loudness of 130 dB is the *threshold of pain*. It is the point at which you begin to *feel* sound—in the form of pain—in addition to *hearing* it.

A good-quality microphone will not overload at these pressures. The distortion of a well constructed microphone can be held to 0.5 percent, or even less, with sound pressures of up to 130 dB. Some professional microphones can be used in the mouth of a trumpet, which can produce a loudness of up to 146 dB. Even under such extreme working conditions, the output of the microphone remains clean, that is, *undistorted*. However, such high sound pressure levels result in extraordinarily high signal output levels from the microphone. This high signal output voltage, fed into a following tube or transistor amplifier, can overload the amplifier, driving it into distortion levels.

An amplifier or recorder input sensitivity rating describes the absolute, maximum amount of voltage or power it can handle before it overloads and distorts the signal. A comparison of various input sensitivities reveals a surprising variation. Some amplifiers may have a −60 dB input signal rating, meaning it will handle a signal of this level before overloading. Others can tolerate up to −22 dB output from the microphone without distorting. Unfortunately, there is no standard, and there cannot be since microphones are never used at the same distance. Also, sound-pressure sources are of infinite variety and loudness.

As an example, consider a sound pressure level of 94 dB applied to the diaphragm of a microphone, such as the AKG Model D-190. This will now produce a catalog output rating of −53 dB. But if the sound pressure is raised by 36 dB, the microphone output will be the original output of −53 dB plus 36 dB more. The output is now −17 dB. Smaller negative numbers mean higher output, getting closer to the 1 volt or 1 milliwatt reference point, or 0 dB

We now have an ouput signal of −17 dB. Assume, now, that our amplifier has a −60 dB input rating. This means our microphone output is 43 dB higher than this amplifier input rating. Even if we were to use an amplifier that can handle

−22 dB without distorting, the output from the microphone is still 5 dB above that figure.

What will happen depends, in part, on whether the amplifier receiving the signal from the microphone is a tube amplifier or a solid-state unit using transistors. Tube amplifiers will give a small warning in slightly increased, sometimes tolerable, distortion when the input overload point is reached. If the amplifier uses transistors it will sound clean to the overload point and will then go into sudden, often violent, distortion.

Many professional recording consoles supply input attenuation with selectable degrees of voltage-reducing pads or electronically variable input-stage gain sensitivity. Some portable, high-fidelity recorders have a provision for modular, immediately replaceable microphone input amplifiers of different sensitivities. In-line pads are also available for use between the microphone cable and amplifier. You can use such pads when you know in advance that the input sound levels are going to be extraordinarily high, as in the case of a rock concert. With rock music, microphone working distances are often very small. When recording classical music, sound pressure level decreases, since the microphone working distance is usually much greater.

You can buy signal attenuation pads for use between the microphone cable and amplifier, that supply a typical 10 dB or 20 dB voltage reduction from the microphone. The pad can be mounted in or near the amplifier and switched out when not needed. It is much better to use such an attenuation pad rather than selecting a low output microphone to compensate for close-use, high-loudness applications. The disadvantage of choosing a low output microphone is that you lose the advantage of better signal-level-to-noise ratios in normal use, and you could end up with a poorer frequency response. It is always a safe procedure—a *good* procedure—to buy the best microphone possible for all applications. You can always control end-system response and microphone output voltage with various accessories. Reducing the microphone input level to the amplifier is easily done, and solves the problem of "microphone overload."

MICROPHONE SPECIFICATIONS

Microphones are often bought on the basis of frequency response and polar pattern only, but this isn't enough. While a

111

microphone is a separate component, it is a part of a complete electronic amplification system, and this sytem can never be better than its weakest link. When reading microphone specs, look for information over and beyond frequency-response and directivity characteristics. Microphone specs usually list microphone output level and loading characteristics. You must have this data to make certain that the microphone and its following amplifier will work well together as a team.

There are three basic requirements which should appear in the microphone spec sheet. These are:

1—The *output* of the microphone, in either a voltage or power ratio. Often the output is in the form of decibels (and that is always a ratio or comparison with some reference level), such as −55 dB.

2—The *internal impedance* of the microphone, supplied in ohms. The actual value isn't critical, and is sometimes indicated as either low impedance or high impedance.

3—The amount of *sound pressure* applied. As indicated earlier, this can be supplied in several different ways, such as 1 mW/10 microbars. This corresponds to 94 dB sound pressure level (SPL).

European manufacturers often specify microphone output voltage in terms of millivolts per microbar when the microphone is unloaded—when the microphone is not connected to the following amplifier input. American manufacturers specify output voltage in maximum power output, as expressed in dBM when the microphone is loaded with its characteristic impedance—when the microphone works into an amplifier whose input impedance is similar to the impedance of the microphone. (Dbm is simply the decibel referred to 1 milliwatt.) The sound pressure applied is often expressed as referenced to 1 mW/10 dynes/cm^2. This is equal to 1 mW/10 microbars and this, in turn, is equal to 94 dB SPL.

When a microphone is to be used with a very short working distance, you should know the sound pressure level which will produce a specified level of distortion. Above this point the microphone diaphragm will produce excessive distortion. Distortion above 1.0 percent is unacceptable and the sound pressure levels reaching the microphone diaphragm must be kept below this point. For condenser microphones, the self-noise level of the mike and its dynamic range are important specifications.

MICROPHONE SPECS AS GUIDELINES

Microphone specifications are useless unless they can be interpreted into meaningful guidelines. Most low-impedance microphones are in the 150-ohm impedance classification, with an actual impedance ranging from 100 to 300 ohms. Such microphones are specified with 94 dB SPL applied. When the microphone output voltage is specified as −50 dBm output, that microphone is 10 dB more sensitive than one rated at −60 dBm. Since conversational speech at a 1 foot distance from the microphone is about 65 dB SPL, the 94 dB SPL used for a microphone rating is typical of a pop vocalist or instrumentalist. Some vocalists, however, practically put the microphone inside their mouth and extremely high sound levels are produced. As an example, a professional condenser microphone with a specified output of −40 dBm produced a measured output of +5 dBm from a vocalist at mouth-touching range. Such a high signal output practically demands the inclusion of a line-level input control to reduce the signal voltage below the overloading point of the following amplifier.

It is important to recognize when excessive sound pressure level produces distortion. In 99 percent of the applications, the input amplifier connected to the microphone will overload long before the microphone diaphragm reaches its limits.

IMPEDANCE

Impedance, like resistance, is opposition to current flow. Either resistance or impedance can be compared to friction. A certain amount is not only desirable, but essential. Extremes, such as close to zero friction or unusually high friction, are undesirable. If the friction of a road is almost zero, there is no way in which a car can move forward, a condition that sometimes arises on a highly iced road. If the road friction is unusually high, such as a road that has many layers of wet clinging mud, excessive energy is used in moving the car forward. While resistance and impedance are both measured in ohms, impedance includes the electrical opposition not only of resistors, but other components, such as coils and capacitors.

Microphones are alternating-current generators and, as such, have both internal resistance and electrical impedance. Their source impedance is usually measured at 1 kHz (1000

Hz). And to emphasize the fact that the microphone is really an AC generator, you could connect a very sensitive, very-low wattage, electric light across it and this light would flicker *on* and *off* as it received sound from a voice or instrument.

All microphones have a certain amount of impedance. Impedance in electronic components, though, can be a frequency-sensitive function, and to say a component has an output impedance of 200 ohms simply means that this is its impedance at a particular frequency.

Low-impedance, moving-coil dynamic microphones have typical impedance values in the range of 50 to 250 ohms, more usually 150 to 200 ohms. Microphones with a 200 ohm impedance, such as AKG dynamics, require more skill in design and manufacturing but are more efficient than those having lower impedances. An additional benefit is that the impedance is less affected by changes in frequency.

Since all moving-coil dynamic microphones are inherently low-impedance types, a transformer is needed for conversion to high impedances, such as 25,000 ohms and higher. Some dynamic microphones have built-in transformers to supply this required impedance transformation. Such mikes often have a provision for bypassing the transformer for alternate connection directly to the moving coil inside the microphone. Such mikes, then, are low/high-impedance types, depending on the setting of the switch that controls inclusion or exclusion of the transformer.

If the microphone does not have a built-in transformer, in-line accessory transformers are available and microphone cables with a transformer at the amplifier input enables a quick impedance change by substituting a low-impedance cable.

Impedance Matching

The output of the microphone is connected to the input of a preamplifier. Like the microphone, the preamp has a certain amount of impedance and, since the signal produced by the microphone is fed to the input of the preamp, what we are talking about is its *input impedance*. Ideally, the input impedance of the preamp should be identical with that of the microphone. In practice this never happens. You might have identical impedances at one particular sound frequency, but not at others. All we need concern ourselves with is that the input impedance of the preamp should reasonably approximate the output impedance of the microphone. If both are designated by their respective manufacturers as low impedance, there is no point in playing a numbers game.

The advantage of having impedance matching is to get optimum transfer of signal from the microphone to the amplifier. If the amplifier has an input impedance similar to that of the microphone—a condition known as *impedance matching*—the maximum amount of signal will be transferred from the microphone to the amplifier.

Offhand, this sounds highly desirable and extremely efficient. However, if you use a preamp having an adequately high input sensitivity and a microphone with a reasonable signal voltage output, you will be able to "throw away" signal. The theory that if a little is good, a lot is better, does not apply to the microphone signal output. Feeding too much microphone signal into a preamp is just as bad, probably worse, than feeding in too little. Excessive signal input, as mentioned earlier, results in signal clipping, a serious form of distortion. And while some signal is lost through impedance mismatching, much more is deliberately thrown away through the use of resistive attenuator networks working between the output of the microphone and the input of the preamp.

If you divide all microphones, regardless of type, into two categories, *low* or *high* impedance, then you simplify your microphone buying decision. Further, any number of tape recorders or preamplifiers give you your choice. They supply a high-impedance microphone input, a low-impedance microphone input, or both.

Constancy of Impedance

Components such as capacitors and coils are frequency sensitive—their opposition to the flow of current changes with frequency. This characteristic is not true of resistors, a component whose opposition to current flow is not dependent on frequency. The output impedance of the most widely used quality microphones for high-fidelity sound, and that includes dynamic and condenser mikes (and ribbon mikes as well) is almost purely resistive. This means that the output impedance of these microphones remains fairly constant over the entire audio frequency range.

Professional recordists generally select low-impedance dynamics, since they can then have the option of using long cables without being particularly concerned about picking up noise or hum. If your amplifier or tape deck has a high-impedance input only, you can get a matching transformer, known as a *line matching transformer*, that will let you couple a low-impedance microphone to the high-impedance input of the deck. But most tape decks are now solid-state and they do not present microphone connection problems.

Low or High Impedance?

Basically, any microphone can be manufactured as *high* or *low* impedance. Low-impedance connections are more desirable and your choice should be a low-impedance microphone connected to the low-impedance input of your recorder or amplifier. The advantage of low impedance is that it means less susceptibility to hum and electrical noise pickup by the connecting cable run over long distances and with no audible loss of high-frequency response over long cable distances. You can use an XLR-type audio connector, which permits adding cable lengths up to 1000 feet without interference, hum pickup, or loss of high frequencies.

Since a low impedance microphone seems to have so many advantages, why bother with high-impedance mikes? A high-impedance microphone will produce a larger output signal than a low-impedance unit for a given sound source. This higher output enables equipment designers to cut costs in amplifier design by eliminating transformers and pre-amplifier stages. In other words, if a manufacturer sells a combination microphone and preamp, he is more likely to use a high-impedance microphone, since this permits him to cut down on preamp circuitry and reduce manufacturing costs. In the case of "budget type" amplifiers and recorders, a high-impedance microphone may be required in order to be able to supply enough input signal voltage.

The useful distance between the microphone amplifier and the high-impedance microphone is about 20 feet. A greater length of cable will cause a loss of high-frequency response due to cable capacitance. Further, as cable length is increased there is greater susceptibility to hum and radio-frequency interference pickup. Finally, the phone-plug connectors which are used with high-impedance microphone cable don't always provide a positive connection. This results in a static-like noise and can possibly result in intermittent operation.

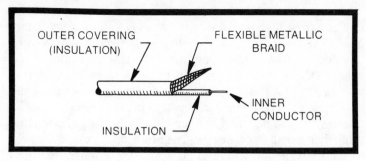

Fig. 4-6. An unbalanced microphone cable.

However, if the connecting cable to a high-impedance microphone is kept to a reasonable length, 25 feet or less, then the problems associated with long cable distances aren't ordinarily bothersome. For many practical installations, cable runs of less than 25 feet are common and acceptable. This length is sufficient for use in home recording, conference recording, group-sound reinforcement systems, television news reporting, and many similar applications.

For the amateur recordist, the choice of which impedance microphone to buy is usually dictated by existing equipment. If the equipment has a low Z (low impedance) input, get a low-impedance microphone. High impedance input? Get a high Z mike. If it has both, get a low-impedance microphone.

When we get into the area of professional recording, long microphone cable runs become necessary. Professional applications require much longer microphone cable runs in studios, auditoriums, and in any large-area reinforcement systems applications.

Microphone impedance has no relationship to microphone quality or price. A high-impedance microphone could be cheaper or more expensive than a low-impedance mike. The shape, weight, and durability of the microphone are also completely unrelated to its impedance. Complaints of poor results with microphones are almost always due to improper connections or wrong impedance matching despite the fact that the microphone user has a choice only of low or high impedance.

CABLES

Cable is the word used to describe the wire (or wires) used to lead the electrical signal produced by the microphone to some device that will work on the signal, such as an amplifier. Cables can be high impedance or low. A high-impedance cable, also called *unbalanced line* (Fig. 4-6), consists of a wire (conductor) that passes lengthwise through the center of the cable. This wire is surrounded by some type of insulating material with a flexible metal braid put on the outside of the insulating material. Since the braid is made of metal, it can be used as a conductor, and in a technical sense, unbalanced line really has a double conductor. The braid also works as a shield to keep interfering voltages, such as hum or other electrical noise, from reaching the central conductor, sometimes called the "hot" lead. The *braid*, also referred to as *shield braid*, is the "cold" or ground lead. The shield braid, however, isn't too effective in preventing signal interference.

A *balanced* line (Fig. 4-7) consists of two inner conductors instead of one. Both conductors, running the length of the cable, are fully insulated from each other. A flexible metal shield also surrounds the insulation, but in this case the shield, made of flexible metallic braid, is not part of the signal path and is used as a means of keeping interfering signals out.

UNBALANCED INPUTS

A low-to-high impedance transformer in the amplifier, is required for voltage gain and balanced signal isolation of ground circuits to minimize hum and radio-interference pickup. Many tape recorders and some public-address amplifiers provide unbalanced, low-impedance, phone-plug input connections. Such circuitry may be satisfactory for home recording and use in interference-free areas, but balanced, transformer-coupled input circuits are preferable for trouble-free service.

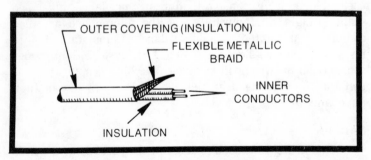

Fig. 4-7. A balanced microphone cable.

Many manufacturers supply combination high/low-impedance microphones with connections for user option at the termination end of the cable. Sometimes there is confusion if the microphone terminations are changed from *high* to *low* impedance for various uses and the wrong connection is made when the opposite termination is most needed. AKG's solution to this problem is to supply all microphones with balanced XLR low-impedance connections. An accessory 20-foot cable with a low-to-high impedance transformer is built into the phone plug termination. This converts any low-impedance microphone to high-impedance. Further benefits of this system are:

1—No confusion about impedance
2—No high-frequency loss because the high-impedance output is within the shielded phone plug, a maximum high-frequency cable length of 2 inches, and
3—Elimination of hum and intermittent connections due to the loss of shielding in a high-impedance cable.

Most consumer tape recorders feature unbalanced low-impedance microphone inputs specified at 150 to 1000 ohms and higher. Any low-impedance mike will work properly with these machines and, as long as the impedance of the recorder input is higher than that of the microphone, exact termination matching is not important. When connecting a three-wire low-impedance microphone to an unbalanced input connector, fasten the wire connected to pin 2 of the three-pin connector at the other end of the cable to the signal or "hot" pin of the unbalanced connector. Connect the remaining two wires to the unbalanced connector shield or ground point. Connections between the second audio wire and the cable shield are necessary for proper operation. After connecting your microphone, should you find the volume weak and the sound quality "tinny," check and make certain that the second audio wire is connected with the cable shield at the ground point on the connector. Cable capacitance will provide the tinny sound if the signal *minus* and *ground* connections aren't fastened together properly.

TWO MICROPHONES—ONE INPUT

In some instances it may be necessary to connect two microphones to one input. In such a case, wire the microphones in series so that the internal impedance of one microphone will not load the other microphone, causing a loss of quality and sound level.

THE SOUND REINFORCEMENT SYSTEM

The simplest sound reinforcement system would consist of a single microphone with its output connected to a preamplifier, followed by a power amplifier and a single speaker. But while it has the advantage of low cost, it is a limited setup.

A more elaborate arrangement would consist of an audio console containing a preamplifier/mixer arrangement which would accept the outputs of a number of microphones. A unit of this kind would have individual gain controls for each microphone, plus fixed line attenuation pads of −10 dB and −20 dB. It would also contain an equalizer to compensate for recording-room acoustics.

Following the audio console would be one or more stereo power amplifiers, connected to pairs of speakers. The speakers could have built-in crossover networks designed to separate the audio frequencies into two or more channels for distribution to bass speakers (woofers), midrange speakers (squawkers), and treble speakers (tweeters). In some setups an electronic crossover is connected between the preamplifier and its following power amplifier.

FRONT-TO-BACK DISCRIMINATION

Front-to-back discrimination indicates, in decibels, how much unwanted sound or noise is being rejected to the rear, over the frequency range of the microphone. The frequency response of a microphone may sometimes be supplied in *double graph* form. The frequency response of the microphone is plotted with the sound "head on", that is, at 0° on the polar pattern. Another graph is plotted with the sound directed at the microphone "tail", the 180° point.

Figure 4-8 shows a representative pair of frequency-response curves for a cardioid. The bottom curve indicates that the suppression is being maintained at all frequencies. Slight variations at the two extremes of the frequency response ranges are acceptable.

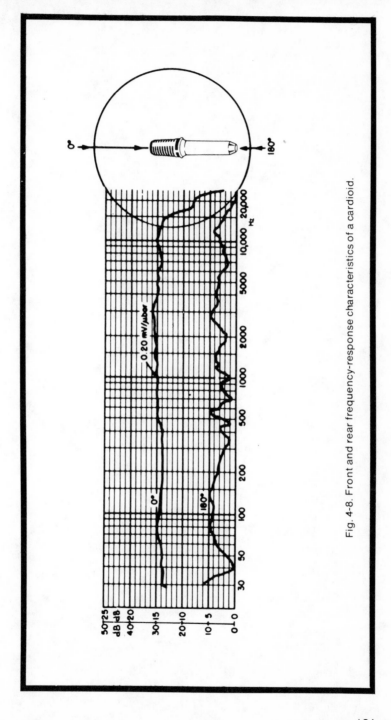

Fig. 4-8. Front and rear frequency-response characteristics of a cardioid.

Chapter 5
How to Use Microphones:
General Applications

HOW TO USE MICROPHONES:
GENERAL APPLICATIONS

Before you invest in one or more microphones, and to avoid the letdown that comes with impulse buying, there are certain decisions you should make. What type of microphone do you want (dynamic or condenser); what type of sound-collection pattern (omni, cardioid, shotgun, or differential); low or high impedance, and, finally, how much do you wish to spend?

You do not need to be an engineer to be able to read microphone specification sheets, to look at and understand polar patterns, to examine sensitivity numbers and frequency response curves. However, you cannot plug specs sheets into your sound system. Technical measurements and response-curve information in microphone catalogs and spec sheets are prepared by engineers for engineers and technically oriented people. But the information that is supplied is often just for comparison purposes. However, you cannot *hear* a microphone catalog or spec sheet. In the final analysis it is microphone performance that counts.

Does this mean spec sheets have no value? On the contrary. They can give you an excellent guide as to what you may expect from a microphone, but it is the actual performance that is the final criterion. And even here final performance does not mean that you can put a microphone anywhere and expect it to give you the results you want. Listening to music is a subjective experience and, while there are some general guidelines about microphone setups, the best way to make microphone specs meaningful is to work with mikes in a real, live recording situation.

Microphone manufacturers test microphones in two ways. Microphone performance must be measured according to established standards for comparative technical data in an anechoic chamber—a specially designed room all of whose surfaces are completely lined with sound absorbing material. This type of room does not generate any sound of its own, nor does it reflect sound. An anechoic chamber, though, has absolutely no comparison with live recording in your own room, for the acoustic qualities of your recording room are entirely different. Microphone manfuacturers also check mikes in live recording situations, but the problem here is that no two recording rooms are the same. The recording room can and *does* have a tremendous influence on the sound. And even if the manufacturer could manage to simulate your personal recording room, there is no assurance that he would use the same number of microphones, the same types of mikes, that the performer and instruments would be the same, that the sound pressure level would be the same, and that the mikes would be positioned in precisely the same manner. This represents quite a large number of variables.

The situation sounds hopeless, but it isn't. You don't need to be an engineer to read a polar pattern, or to understand that one microphone can be more sensitive than another, or to comprehend frequency response and other technical characteristics of microphones. You can have a true appreciation of microphone specs, and such an appreciation and understanding is important. But it is just a *first step*. In the final analysis, after you buy your mikes, you must learn how to use them and live with them. A quality microphone can give you the sound you want, but that doesn't necessarily mean you will get that sound immediately and automatically. You and your microphones must form a partnership or a marriage. Call it what you like, but *cooperation* is the key word. So cooperate!

SOME DO'S AND DON'TS OF RECORDING

It is very easy to become accustomed to noise and, unless you make yourself deliberately conscious of the existence of a noise or noises, you may not be aware they exist. In some instances it is the absence of noise, rather than its presence, which we may find disturbing. We expect to hear the noise of a closing door. We expect an electric fan to hum slightly or to make some kind of a fan-blade sound. We expect to hear footsteps on a bare, wood floor. And we are so accustomed to the sounds we make when we breathe that we aren't aware of them.

The reason for this is that the human brain has the ability to discriminate, to pick and choose. But the microphone does not. What it "hears" within its pickup range it will reproduce as an electrical signal. That signal will be amplified and recorded on tape right along with your music. The difference is that you will now be listening rather critically to the music and so, for the first time you will be hearing noises you never noticed before: first, because you are now conscious of them; second, because they have been amplified. As a first step in the use of microphones, stand still and listen. Listen hard. You may now hear street noises, or noises elsewhere in your home—a voice, the telephone, the ringing of door chimes, the movement of people in other rooms, or whatever. You may hear your own breathing. And then you will realize that the world is a noisy place—and so it is.

You may also have one or more people in your recording room for various reasons—the performer or performers, someone to help you in making the recording, or just an observer. But the greater the number of people, the higher the noise level. People breathe, they move, and chairs move with them. They sneeze or cough or do some throat-clearing.

The only one that should be holding a microphone would be a vocalist who must move around. For home recording there should be no reason why this microphone cannot be boom mounted. Mount all your microphones in booms having decent suspensions. It doesn't do your recording any good to have people bumping into booms, so a general word of caution for everyone to remain in position once the recording has started is in order. Movement, however, is part of most musicians' repertoire, so make allowance for just what it is that the musicians will do. A dry run will possibly give you some idea of what to expect.

Use a windscreen on your microphones for outdoor recording, or indoors when you have a singer doing some really close-in vocals. If you are troubled with popping in vocals, try having the singer slant his or her sound output across the microphone head instead of right into it.

You may find that cardioids tend to be "bass happy" when brought close to the sound source. This is something to remember if you want more bass response, or, conversely, if you want less.

HOW MANY MICROPHONES?

The minimum number of microphones, of course, is *one*, but one-mike recording, except for voice interviews, means you are going nowhere. This doesn't mean you can't record music with one microphone—you can. But with just one mike, your output will be mono, not stereo. Furthermore, with just one microphone there is no chance for experimenting with microphones having different polar patterns. The only thing you can do with a single microphone is move it around to see what effect it will have on the recording.

Professional recording studios use a number of microphones and, at the present time, it seems as though they are using an individual microphone for each particular instrument. The output of each of these individual microphones is brought into a separate track on tape, using a multichannel tape recorder—with as many as 24, or more, tracks. In the studio, the instruments are very close to the mikes, and in some instances the microphones are in the instrument. As a consequence, the sound output is initially very dry, with extremely little reverberant sound. This makes adjustment of the bass and treble controls and an inclusion of artificial reverberation a part of the tape-recording process.

In the studio, all the instruments can be recorded at the same time, but they may also be recorded separately. The tracks are then *mixed* down to a two-channel master, with the sound ultimately appearing on a stereo disc.

Of course, there are exceptions to every rule. In the professional mike field, the SM 69 stereo condenser mike by Neumann consists of two separate and independent mike capsule systems mounted one above the other. The upper element can be rotated up to 270° with respect to the lower. This enables the user to apply various intensity stereo recording techniques. Both mike systems are remote controllable and can be switched independently in 9 steps to cardioid, figure 8, and omni patterns with six characteristics in between. The mike can also be used as two mono units, as, for example, when two mikes with differing directional patterns are needed in the same place. Axis of maximum sensitivity is at right angles to the mike body. The SM 69 is intended for stereo recording applications where the original sound picture, in its natural acoustics, is to be reproduced.

With two or, preferably, three mikes, you are set for home recording. You can mix sounds—and with the typical home recorder what you mix is what you get. But you still have an advantage, since you can always rerecord. In a professional recording studio, time is money. Recording, mixing, equalizing, and adding reverb are all part of a professional routine. In your home, with your own equipment and your own mikes, you can experiment as much and as freely as you want.

There is a big difference between listening to live sounds and listening to recorded sound. Recording does not necessarily mean that your goal is an absolutely faithful reproduction of the musicians' sound. You can create all sorts of sonic impressions. A competent recordist can be regarded as much of an artist as the performers.

TRACKS VS CHANNELS

These two words—*tracks* and *channels*—are so related to each other they are sometimes regarded as being synonymous. Channels means the number of tracks that are recorded or played back at any one time. Thus, *stereo* is the same as two channel, *quadraphonic* is the same as four channel. Two-channel sound indicates that one channel will be reproduced by the left speaker and the other channel by the right speaker.

The number of tracks means the number of paths on the tape on which sound can be recorded. Open-reel tape, for example, has four tracks. When used for stereo recording and playback, one of the tracks is for left-channel sound, the other for right-channel sound. You listn to these two channels with the tape moving in one direction. However, since the tape has four tracks, and you have used only two of them, you can use the other two, also for stereo recording, except that now the tape will move in the other direction.

You can use open-reel tape for quadraphonic recording because it does have four channels. However, you pay a price, and that is you effectively cut recording and playing time in half. If you want to record quadraphonic sound on open-reel tape you will need all four tracks. Two of the tracks will be for front left- and right-sound; the remaining two tracks will be for back left- and right-sound.

Cartridge tape has eight tracks. You need a pair of tracks for stereo and 8-track has four pairs of two channels for stereo, two pairs of four channels for quadraphonic sound.

Cassette tape has four tracks, supplying two pairs of stereo channels, with one pair in one direction, the other pair in the other direction.

MULTI-TRACK RECORDING

Multi-track recording means recording different parts of the music separately until the output of an entire musical group is down on tape. A variety of recording techniques is possible.

Good multi-track recording can't be done on a hit-or-miss basis. You must have some sort of plan or guide. You'll find it helpful to start with the drums, which supply the beat, giving the correct number of bars that will be needed. You'll also need a "tap in" signal, a signal that will be the clue to the first musical beat.

One of the great advantages of tape, of course, is that you can check your progress as you go along. After recording rhythm and bass, you can then *dub in* the melody.

WORKING DISTANCE

Working distance is the amount of separation, in inches, feet, or any other unit of distance measurement, between the sound source and the diaphragm of the microphone. Sound pressure level decreases 6 dB every time the distance is doubled. Six decibels is a four-to-one ratio. If you place a microphone 1 foot from the instrument of a performer and then decide to change that separation to 2 feet, the sound pressure level in the vicinity of the diaphragm of the microphone will be one-fourth its original value. If you now move the microphone to a distance of four feet (doubling the distance), you will get another 6 dB decrease in sound pressure level.

The decrease of SPL by 6 dB every time the working distance is doubled is applicable to dry sound only and does not include reverberant sounds. It is much more applicable to out-of-doors recording, where there is little or no reverb, than to an indoor miking situation, where the walls, floor, and ceiling can supply substantial reverb. The amount by which sound pressure level will drop as the microphone is moved away from the sound source is greater for a "dead" room, a room with little reverb, than it is for a "live" room, a room whose surfaces reflect sound rather well.

MONITORING

A musician has at least two important considerations. The first is the *quality* of sound output of his own instrument. The other is the *relationship* of his sound to the sound of all the other instruments in the group. In effect, then, what he tries to do is to listen to both.

If the sound is not being recorded, the total sound is that produced by the performers. Depending on room acoustics, the total sound at the listener's ears can be quite different from the dry sound in the immediate vicinity of the performers. If the sound is being picked up by a number of microphones, if it is being mixed, then another variable has been included in addition to room acoustics. Add to this the fact that the loudspeakers being used to bring sound to all parts of the audience can supply their own sound coloration.

Stage monitors are sometimes used to direct sound to the performers, letting them hear the results of their own contribution to overall sound. Conceivably, the performers could hear the audience speakers, but these are generally positioned facing the audience and so speaker sound may not be that audible to the performers. Speakers positioned to direct amplified sounds to the performers are known as *stage monitors*.

While monitoring is sometimes done with headphones, tape playback is often done through speakers. The problem is that headphone sound and speaker sound are quite different. A lot depends on the kind of headphones you use. If the headphones don't provide a good acoustic seal for the ears, you will be listening to extraneous sound as well as any recorded sound. While open-air phones are fine for playback listening, they aren't suitable for a recording session.

MICROPHONE PLACEMENT

It is generally not possible to modify the acoustic environment in which recording is to take place. If you are going to record an orchestra, the number of people in the audience and the noise level they produce are beyond control. Not much can be done for an in-home recording situation unless you want to make a determined effort to change the acoustic characteristics of that room. However, a variable is available that gives you some control of recorded sound—the *placement* of the microphones.

Two extremes for microphone placement are possible. One is to mike close in, the other is to have the performer and microphone widely separated. The first arrangement helps eliminate room acoustics; the other includes room acoustics in the recording.

Like any other extreme situation, adoption of such microphone recording techniques does not produce satisfactory results. Recording very close is equivalent to putting your ears very close to a sound source. This is an unnatural listening position, for you will hear the pure, direct, dry sound of the instrument or voice sounds just as though you had decided you wanted to do such close-in listening. We are much more accustomed to sound at spectator distance.

This does not mean to say that mikes aren't handled in this way. Professional recording people do use mikes close to screaming voices, inside bass drums, in string bass bridges, near the mouth of brass instruments, and just over the strings inside a piano, for example.

Consider what would happen if you put your ears in such a position. Not only would the sound seem unnatural, but with high sound pressure levels you would suffer physical discomfort, if not acute pain.

What happens when a microphone is worked this way? All the microphone does is generate a very high output voltage. Unless there is a pad in the line preceding the preamplifier input, it is possible that the high voltage produced by the microphone will overload the input-signal handling capabilities of the preamp, leading to *distortion*.

This doesn't mean you cannot work a microphone close in. You may want to produce certain sound effects or you may want to emphasize the dry sound of an instrument. To some listeners the rasp of strings being played or the sound of sliding fingers along steel or gut wires adds realism. But if this is what you want, then use a microphone attenuation pad in the cable to reduce microphone output voltage to a level the following amp can handle. You can always remove the pad for more distant microphone use when the output voltage won't be so high. The attenuation pad is resistive and if correctly designed and constructed will not affect frequency response. Professional recording equipment in studios provides built-in microphone voltage attenuation circuitry so as to be able to control microphone output voltage satisfactorily. Remember that no good-quality microphone will overload and produce audible distortion when compared with that possible in the rest of the reproduction chain. A noise-cancelling, differential-design microphone is the only type which must be used very close to the source and isn't suitable for distance pickup. Such mikes are useful when it is necessary to reject distant sounds, primarily in noisy commercial environments for more intelligible voice communications.

MICROPHONE COMPARATIVE ANALYSIS

An omni collects sound from all directions with equal sensitivity. You can use an omni between two performers or surrounded by a group, knowing that all sounds will be picked up with equal loudness. However, the same microphone will be equally sensitive to room acoustics in all directions. This has its advantages but also its disadvantages. In a normal listening pattern we are accustomed to hearing total-surround sound. However, when listening to music many people resent distracting extraneous sounds. In the total family of variations in microphone sound-collecting patterns, and this includes omni, cardioid, supercardioids, and shotguns, all will "spotlight" when used close in and pick up over a wider area with increasing distance from the source. And so even with an omni the amount of ambient sound picked up depends on the working distance of the microphone. Keep in mind that an omni, a well-constructed omni, will pick up sound equally well from all sources, but that not all sources have the same loudness level. An omni, worked in at very close range to an extremely loud sound source, will reproduce that sound source in proportion to its level and the ambient sound in proportion to its level. But when two sounds of greatly different level, such as loud direct and weak ambient, are recorded, the much louder sound tends to cover or hide the weaker, a condition known as *masking effect*. With a relatively loud direct-sound source, with the omni having a very short working distance and much weaker background sound, the background sound may not even be heard in playback. This sound hasn't disappeared; it has just been covered or masked. You can use this recording technique if the only microphone available to you is an omni and you have a recording situation in which background noise cannot be eliminated and would be distracting.

Similarly, when using a single omni to record a group of singers and you want equal distribution of sound, position the stronger singers somewhat back from the microphone, the weaker singers in more closely. There is no reason for vocalists to form a perfect circle around the omni, for you can position them to get the recorded sound you want. Recording is more than just a matter of sticking a microphone in front of performers. Since you ordinarily cannot change the acoustic setup of the recording room, you still have the option of positioning the performers and the microphone to overcome or compensate for acoustic recording conditions. It does take some experimentation, but fortunately tape is a medium that lets you do just that, over and over again, as you wish. And just as a practical demonstration, you can record with an omni pointed away from a voice or full orchestra, with the connector-end pointed toward the sound source, and you will still pick up the direct sound as though the microphone were directed normally at the performers. Further, you cannot, during playback, be aware of the backward positioning of the microphone, or even if the omni had been positioned sideways. With an omni, it is *working distance* that counts, not the way the microphone is positioned.

The omnis are a rather neglected type of microphone. They should be more popular than they are, for they add considerable flexibility to any recording situation, whether in a professional studio or in the home. Cardioids are more often used for recording, far outnumbering omnis and shotguns. Omnis are usually a second choice and will continue in this capacity until users learn how to take advantage of their versatility.

The basic directional cardioid microphone is an acoustic computer. It is programmed for maximum sensitivity in the forward direction and gradually reduces its sensitivity a little to sounds arriving at 90° and becomes relatively weak to any sounds arriving from the rear of the microphone. Thus, the cardioid has a preferred direction for maximum loudness pickup. There is a common misconception that the cardioid shuts off rear sound much as you would use a door to get isolation from noise. Actually, the cardioid is just relatively insensitive to sound arriving from the connector end. Useful sound is received over a very wide angle in all forward directions and it collects far less sound from the rear. The sound shutoff isn't perfect, though, and it would be unreasonable to assume that the microphone forms a perfect barrier against rear sound. Because it does collect far less sound from the rear, however, the cardioid can suppress more room sound and noise than an omni in the same position subjected to an identical sound field.

One of the other advantages of the cardioid is its better coverage at longer working distances. Live classical and small group recordists working in stereo often use a pair of cardioids because of this characteristic.

Because the cardioid's front-to-back sound signal pickup is greater than the omni's, you can work the cardioid in close and take advantage of masking effect to eliminate background sound level when such level cannot be controlled otherwise.

Microphones with a bidirectional, figure-eight pattern are available, but aren't often used in recording. You can get two-direction monophonic pickup with the two sound sources on opposite sides of one omni or cardioid pointing vertically up between them. You can also use two cardioids, tail-to-tail at 180° for bidirectional stereo pickup.

Supercardioid, and shotgun pattern microphones are just variations of the basic cardioid. Forward coverage may be tighter, sound collected over a narrower angle, but microphone placement is governed by the same application of sound-collection control described earlier.

TWO MIKE RECORDING

There is no reason for having any doubts about using just two microphones or having just a simple two-channel recording ability, nor should you be unduly concerned about any lack of bass and treble equalization except on playback. You can get quite good results with a pair of quality microphones and a quality open-reel tape deck.

The professional studio technique of cramming a microphone close to every sound source and remixing all this later into pseudo-stereo is necessary to save time and cost and to get the performers in and out of the studio in the shortest possible time. In the professional studio special effects can be created, and the final playback becomes an art form of its own. However, this isn't related to a natural performance. Against this is the fact that in-home tape decks, especially top-level units, are of professional quality, and a number of them permit recording sound-on-sound, sound-with-sound, echo, and other effects. Various outboard devices, mixers, and equalizers, are now available, and in-home recording can be done more professionally. Your high-quality in-home tape deck is capable of the same performance as studio equipment. Studio recorders do use wider tape to carry more channels, but the quality of the open-reel tape you buy is the same as that used by the studio.

ADVANTAGES OF IN-HOME RECORDING

In-home recording has a number of advantages. Professional studio time is rather expensive—$50 an hour, or more. Using in-home recording, you can have as many "takes" as you wish. You can experiment as much as you want, and then, with experience, you can get a final recording that is precisely to your taste. In your home you can move mikes around, position the performers, and even modify room acoustics somewhat. Finally, your master tape will quite possibly be a one-generation copy, whereas in the studio several generations are necessary from studio master to final recording.

A multiplicity of microphones, when correctly selected and positioned, can supply very gratifying results. But using a larger number of mikes, that is, more than two, does create problems not inherent in the use of two microphones, and it also has the potential for more distorted and unnatural sound. But for in-home recording, you can have immediate playback, and you can evaluate results immediately.

ACOUSTIC PHASE INTERFERENCE

Using a pair of microphones to pick up a lecturer at a podium can result in some difficulties. Assume you have one mike facing the speaker directly and another mike parallel to the first, a short distance away, possibly a few feet, facing some instrument. What we overlook here is that it takes sound a finite time to travel and the voice of the speaker will reach the second mike a short time—a very short time—after the arrival of the same sound at the first mike. This means the sound pressures are out of *step* or out of *phase*. The effects will be additive or subtractive—that is, the sounds will reinforce each other or will oppose. The overall effect will depend on the frequency of the sound at any moment and the amount of separation of the mikes (Fig. 5-1).

MICROPHONE PHASING

When signals are in step or in phase they reinforce each other. If they are completely out of phase and both signals have the same amplitude or strength, they can cancel each other. There are all sorts of possibilities that can exist between these two conditions—you can have a pair of waves that reinforce at certan points of the wave and oppose each other at different points.

In Fig. 5-2 sound from the performer at the left can enter the microphone at the right, and vice versa. Each microphone gets sound from two different sources. However, the sound paths do not have identical lengths and one sound will arrive at a microphone slightly delayed or behind in time of arrival of the more direct sound. Because the two sounds do not reach the microphone diaphragm at exactly the same time, we will

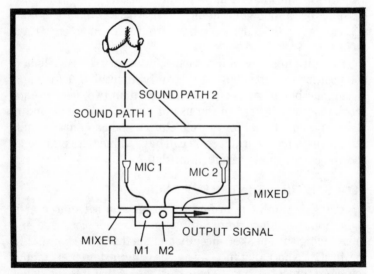

Fig. 5-1. Microphone positioning leading to acoustic phase interference.

136

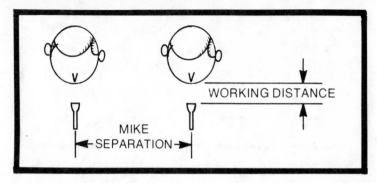

Fig. 5-2. When recording a pair of performers, microphone separation should be at least three times as great as the working distance.

get a combination of sound reinforcement and cancellation. The combined output of the two microphones will result in peaks and dips in the frequency response.

To avoid this problem, make sure the distance between microphones is at least three times the distance between each performer and his individual microphone. If the separation between performer and mike is one foot, then set up the mikes for a separation of not less than three feet.

However, there may be certain miking situations in which a pair of performers must be close to each other. You might, for example, have a male and a female voice and would prefer miking these individually. If you use cardioids, you can bring them closer together by angling them away from each other (Fig. 5-3). In this case the separation between mikes need be only 50 percent greater than that from performer to microphone. If the distance between the performer and

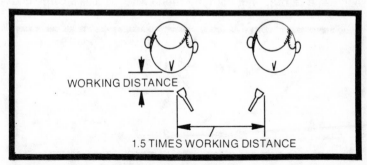

Fig. 5-3. You can minimize sound cancellation by using a pair of cardioids angled away from each other.

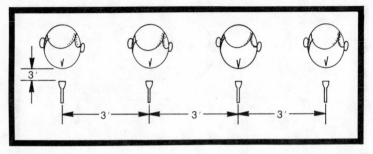

Fig. 5-4. With a larger number of performers, the 3 to 1 separation rule still applies.

microphone is one foot, then the separation can be brought down to 1½ feet.

The same consideration applies when using four mikes to record four performers, as shown in Fig. 5-4. Now the chances for phase cancellation have increased. Thus, microphone number 2 can receive input from three performers, starting from the left. In a case of this sort, while the mikes can be separated fairly exactly, the distance between performers often changes, adding to phase cancellation effects. A better miking arrangement would be to have the performers work in pairs, facing each other, as in Fig. 5-5, with each pair using a common microphone.

When you have a pair of microphones angled in on a single performer (Fig. 5-6) do not separate the mike heads. Instead, angle the heads in toward each other as shown in Fig. 5-7.

Phase Considerations

Two microphones are considered in phase when a common sound source reaching both microphones produces a combined

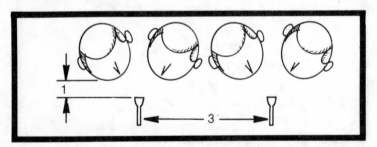

Fig. 5-5. You can mike a group by arranging them in pairs, facing in toward each other and using a microphone for each pair.

138

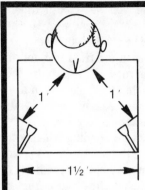

Fig. 5-6. When using a pair of mikes to record a single performer, do not separate the microphones.

output higher than a single microphone. In other words, if a positive pressure were applied to each microphone, a positive voltage would be present at the same output connections on each microphone.

Assuming equal signal strengths, if one microphone is connected in reverse phase from the other, their output voltages would cancel when mixed together. Theoretically, we would have sound going into the microphones, but no voltage coming out of them. In the laboratory it is possible to simulate this condition and the voltage output is indeed zero. In a live situation, the two microphones might not have identical sensitivities, but in any event there would be a substantial reduction in signal output.

Checking Microphone Phasing

Since there is no standardization of microphone phasing within the industry, microphones from one manufacturer can be out of phase when used with microphones from another manufacturer.

Checking the phasing of two microphones only requires a channel mixer that can handle two or more microphones and a VU (*volume unit*) meter. Using voice as a sound source, set the volume level of one microphone at a time for equal VU meter readings. Then position both microphones adjacent to each other and speak into the area between them. If they are in phase, the resulting signal should be 3 dB higher than that produced by one microphone. To see if this is so, switch one microphone off and talk into the area between the two microphones. Make a note of the VU meter reading. Now switch on the unused microphone so you have both mikes working. Talk and note the VU meter reading. If the microphones are in phase there should be a 3 dB increase.

Don't expect to get precisely 3 dB. It's difficult to get an exact reading when a meter pointer is moving. Try to use the same voice level at all times during this test and try to aim your voice at the same "in-between" spot. And of course, your lips should have the same distance from the microphones.

If, instead of getting an increase in dB reading when both mikes are on, you get a decrease, one of the microphones is out of phase with respect to the other. You may not get precisely 3 dB less in signal output, but the reduced flick of the meter when both mikes are connected, compared to that of a single mike, will be enough of an indication that the mikes are out of phase. Since phase is relative to a reference, choose one of the microphones as a reference and phase all the other micrphones to it. If you are trying to get three microphones (or possibly more) in phase, just keep repeating the test. Then select any one of the microphones as your reference and connect all the other microphones so they are in phase with the one you have chosen. It makes no difference which one you choose as your phase reference. You can also do the same without a VU meter, by listening to the sound. Mono mix the microphones for dramatic evidence of phasing.

Importance of Correct Phasing

Why bother with phasing microphones, particularly when it is unlikely that complete sound cancellation will occur, and particularly when the sound input levels may supply more than adequate microphone output levels?

Phase relationships between microphones in a multi-microphone recording session can wreak havoc with the recorded sound unless certain guidelines are observed. If

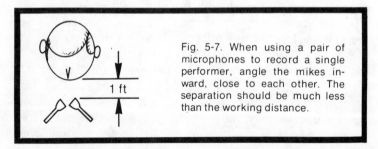

Fig. 5-7. When using a pair of microphones to record a single performer, angle the mikes inward, close to each other. The separation should be much less than the working distance.

microphones are in close proximity to each other, a recording session can become an exercise in frustration. When recording instrumentalists, for example, such as a trumpet player and a sax, the trumpet player's microphone can pick up the sax player's sound, delayed in time depending on the distance between microphones, producing a cancellation of various frequencies in the sax player's sound. If many microphones are used, the combined sound can be badly distorted by these phase cancellations.

A good rule of thumb to use in avoiding phase cancellation is the 3 to 1 rule. The distance to the nearest microphone away from yours should be three or more times the distance from you to your microphone to avoid phase cancellation. For the best sound always use the minimum number of microphones that will give you good sound. What you should follow in good recording practice when using a number of microphones is to make sure the microphones are wired in phase and then space the microphones properly.

Phase cancellation is not only produced by dry or direct sound but can be due to reverberant sound. Sound reflectors, such as walls, tabletops, and microphone stands, can reflect sound back into the side or rear of a microphone, causing phase cancellation. It is easy to run a quick check, taking just a few minutes, to determine if you have this problem. Mount the microphone in the position in which you expect to use it. Talk into the microphone and take a VU reading. If the mike was positioned on a tabletop, lift it about a foot above its surface and repeat your test. If you get a reading of a few decibels more, reflections from the tabletop are causing phase cancellation. The solution in this case, as in other recording situations, is a matter of common sense. If the phase cancellation is due to reflection from a wall, just move the microphone away from it.

Putting Phase to Work

In recording, a fault can sometimes be converted to a benefit. The important thing about out of phase miking is to recognize the fact that it can exist and to know how to take steps to correct it. However, you can use in-phase and out-of-phase microphones to achieve special pickup patterns. If, for example, you are working in an environment with an extremely high noise ambient, you can sometimes improve matters by connecting the microphones out of phase to get noise cancellation. With two cardioid microphones placed back to back and connected in phase you can get an omnidirectional pickup pattern. You can use the same two microphones, connected out of phase, as a bidirectional or figure-8 unit.

There are, of course, a few precautions. The addition or cancellation by phase requires that both microphones be of the same model and closely matched in output and response.

Chapter 6
How to Use Microphones:
Musical Instruments

HOW TO USE MICROPHONES:
MUSICAL INSTRUMENTS

The preceding chapter contains generalized information about microphones, but now we can get down to specifics in the sense that we can discuss the direct application of microphones in selected uses, in this chapter, *musical instruments*.

SOUND COMBINATIONS

There are so many possible vocal and instrument combinations that it is impossible to describe the microphone setup for each and every situation. Enough examples are supplied in the following pages to give you general guidelines for almost any kind of recording problem. It isn't feasible to supply precisely detailed instructions concerning microphone positioning, for there are too many variables. Room acoustics, the number of performers, the instruments used, the various combinations, the number of the types of microphones available will all affect final recording results (Fig. 6-1). There is no way in which you can have an exact "cookbook" approach to recording. However, you must start somewhere and that is the exact purpose of this chapter—to give you your starting point. In any event, even if you should get fair results with your first effort, don't accept it. Tape permits you to record as often as you want, and the first rule in recording is *experimentation*. The playback sound will tell you if you are headed in the right or wrong direction in your recording sessions.

THE PROBLEM OF THE
SOLO INSTRUMENT PERFORMER

One common recording technique for the solo instrument performer is to use either a single or a pair of cardioids to zero in on instrument sound and to cut down background noise as much as possible. Microphone placement can become critical if you are concerned with creating an exact illusion. If you mike in very closely, listening to the reproduced music can supply an impression of huge instrument size (Fig. 6-2). Moving the microphones back away from the performer emphasizes stereo effect, supplying a mental image of a *duo* rather than a *solo*. It can also create the idea that the performer is moving from side to side. A way of overcoming

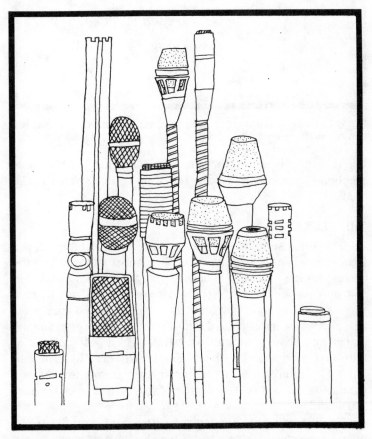

Fig. 6-1. What microphones you select and the way you use them will determine the kind of recorded sound you will get.

Fig. 6-2. Close-in miking can supply an impression of a 'larger-than-natural' instrument size.

this difficulty is to use three microphones: the two cardioids mentioned previously plus a third, either a cardioid or an omni.

THE FLUTE

The flute supplies a rich mixture of middle and upper frequencies. The sharp attack of the flautist's tongue and the corresponding wind sound supply an unmistakable instrumental character. For flute recording you might try a two-way microphone. This provides uniform sound quality off axis and when one is placed midway down the flute, facing the player and about a foot away, you can get a good balance of flute and wind sound without being overly breathy. You can move the microphone closer or farther from the flautist's mouth, depending on the degree of attack and breath sound you want.

To reproduce the distinctive sound of the flute, the microphone should have a smooth, wide-range response across the full range of sound. The microphone should be capable of clean, effortless sound transmission and should supply a slightly bright, "open" sound to lend characteristic airiness.

To reproduce the flute's sound without distortion, position the microphone at right angles to and about 1 foot away from the instrument, or position the microphone midway between the mouth and the flautist's finger position to lessen "over-blow" effect. Place the microphone slightly below and looking upward at the flute so as not to be in a direct line with the air stream. Figure 6-3 provides an example of what *not* to do and is the worst possible position for the microphone.

THE KICK DRUM

Before you record the drum, ask yourself how you want it to sound. You may want it to be as "natural" as possible, but then you may prefer a fuller, heavier bass, or more bass definition, or you may want a tighter drum sound. Your choice

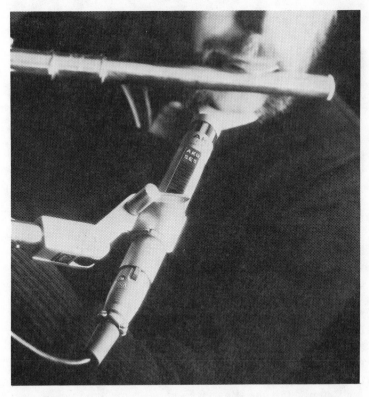

Fig. 6-3. Recording the flute. This is the worst possible position for the microphone.

Fig. 6-4. Recording tom-toms.

of microphone and microphone placement will work together to give you the sound you want to project.

Remove the drum head and put the microphone inside the drum. Try it for sound. Or put the microphone on top of a blanket inside the drum head for the characteristic sound preferred by many professionals in recording. You may also like the sound that results from using a pad of paper towels where the hammer hits the drum to lessen boominess. Don't try to decide in advance; instead, experiment until you get the kind of sound you want.

To get best results you'll need a sensitive microphone, one that responds well to the instrument's timbre, tone delineation, and definition. If you get rattling or buzzing problems with the drum, put masking tape across the drum head to damp out these nuisances.

Drum sets consisting of a snare drum, tom-toms, splash cymbals, hi-hat, and bass drum are common in combos and large dance orchestras. The drum sound will often spill over into other instrumental mikes and may be suitable for recording. If you want a sharp drum sound, pointing an omni condenser microphone down from a boom at the snare drum gives a sharp attack. You get an exciting drive to music when you use this setup in combination with a peak limiter. You can also use a cardioid or omni dynamic microphone in the same position for good results, putting the microphone at the side of the drum head, close to the skin. In this position you can capture the full harmonic texture of the bass drum. You can dampen or muffle the bass drum head as you want for special effects. See Figs. 6-4 and 6-5.

There are other ways of recording the drum set. You can, for example, hang two microphones over the drums, left and right, to get stereo sound. You can also use a separate microphone for each drum. Boom-mount one over the tom-tom

Fig. 6-5. Recording the drum set.

and make certain it is high enough to pick up the cymbals. The microphone over the snare should be sufficiently high to pick up the hi hat. Or you can try using a separate microphone for the hi hat.

If you are planning to record the bass drum by putting the microphone inside, make sure the mike isn't centered because you'll pick up more overtones if it is positioned over to one side. If you are going to mount the microphone off center in the rear you will be working close to the foot pedal. Drum sounds normally override the squeaking of this pedal but your mike may pick up some of the pedal sound. If it does, you must move the microphone away.

REEDS AND BRASS

Reed instruments such as the clarinet, sax, and oboe, and brass instruments such as the trumpet, trombone, french horn, and tuba, are usually recorded as instrumental sections in larger orchestras and as individual performers in small combos. Putting the microphone near the holes of reed instruments will result in the rich tonal coloring of the instrument since woodwinds generate more from holes than the bell. Cardioid microphones for solo instruments and two-way cardioids for reed sections give good results.

In large orchestras, where it is desirable to have separation of sound control between reed sections and the brass sections directly behind them, using a bidirectional microphone or out-of-phase cardioid pair placed back to back will give a full reed sound without brass pickup. The reason for this is that the dead or null side of the bidirectional microphone or figure-eight pattern will be toward the brass.

Brass-instrument soloists often play to the side of a cardioid microphone to reduce the high-frequency bite of the instrument. The reduced high-frequency response at 90° off axis on a single-element cardioid is useful in controlling the brilliance of brass instruments.

You can get a good section blending of instruments when recording brass sections by using cardioid microphones or omnis placed several feet from the section. Of course, if you want greater separation of instruments, use closer microphone placement, as required. Such placement will provide excellent detail to the music, while more distant microphone placement will supply a greater blending of instruments.

It is commonly thought that the sound of reeds all comes out of the bell of the instrument, but this is only partly true. Move up close to a saxophone while it is being played and you will hear some of the sound coming from the finger-hole area. Most of the reed sound comes from the holes or stops. This is more true of the saxophone than any other woodwind. The sound is fairly well distributed between the finger holes and the bell.

THE SAXOPHONE

To record the sax, put the microphone about halfway between the topmost finger holes and the bell of the instrument, with the mike positioned above the instrument and the head of the microphone facing down toward it. (See Fig. 6-6).

Fig. 6-6. Recording the saxophone.

THE CLARINET

When recording a clarinet you will note that almost all the sound comes from the finger holes. Knowing the location of the source of the sound should help in microphone positioning, for you will get the true character of the instrument by aiming the microphone at the main sound source. Trying aiming the microphone along the halfway point of the finger holes.

THE HARMONICA

The harmonica is actually a reed instrument. Its sound output, compared to other reeds, is quite low. Try putting the microphone as closely to the instrument as possible and then listen carefully during playback to determine if you can note any breathing sounds made by the performer. Use a microphone having proximity effect to help bring the bass tones up a bit.

THE DOUBLE OR STRING BASS

The plucked strings of a double bass provide the fundamental tones and rhythm for an instrumental group. In recording low-frequency instruments, such as this one, with close microphone placement, there is a tendency of recordists to confuse proximity effect in a single-element cardioid microphone with extended bass response. Two-way microphones do not exhibit proximity effect and can be effectively placed a few inches from the F hole on the upper side of the bridge of the instrument. Another microphone technique you can try is to use a small, personal microphone such as a lavalier. Wrap the microphone in a layer of foam padding and insert it in the opening of the upper F hole. (See Fig. 6-7). The purpose of the foam is to serve as a shock mount to minimize the transmission of mechanical noise into the microphone. You can hold the padding in place with a rubber band.

To capture the true sound of the bass, think about a small microphone with a neutral, yet full response quality over the entire audio range. The microphone should be small enough to mount in the bridge of the instrument. Properly placed with a foam wraparound, the cardioid pattern should respond well to the mellow sound of the instrument, while reducing "plucking" and "buzzing" sounds from the strings. Some microphones, such as the AKG D-140E cardioid, are suited for this application. It incorporates a specially designed built-in bass rolloff filter, with either normal or rolloff response easily controlled by a recessed switch in the shaft of the microphone. In situations where the bass response may seem too heavy, simply flick the switch for less bass in the rolloff position. Proximity effect is reduced and feedback problems are effectively diminished by proper use of the rolloff switch as well.

In recording the double bass, mount the microphone so the head is slightly above the bridge. Use acoustic foam or sponge as a shock mount. The microphone should not rest directly on the instrument but should be suspended by the sponge.

THE ELECTRIC BASS

The electric bass, or Fender bass, as it is sometimes called, needs amplification to join other instruments. Try a

Fig. 6-7 Recording the double bass. Use acoustic foam or sponge as a shock mount. The sponge is all around. The microphone doesn't rest on the instrument but is suspended.

cardioid or, preferably, a two-way cardioid directly in front of the bass amplifier speaker on axis with the cone of the speaker. Be careful, though. With this kind of positioning and with the electronic amplification supplied by the electric bass it will be easily possible to overdrive the amplifier being supplied with signal by the microphone. You won't damage the microphone, but this is a situation that lends itself easily—too easily—to overload distortion on the part of the amp. You will probably need to use a microphone attenuator pad to prevent recorder or mixer overload. Another method is to use a transformer-type direct box at a point where the bass guitar pickup feeds its amplifier for clearest sound. The purpose of this transformer is to provide a stepped-down voltage suitable for direct connection to a microphone input on the mixer.

THE BANJO

For this instrument, center the microphone on the banjo head. This is the area of maximum sound. Since the banjo has greater sound output than other instruments, such as the acoustic guitar, you may need to pad the microphone down to keep from overloading the amp or mixer.

Another technique for the banjo (or the acoustic guitar) is to mount the microphone on a boom that lets you adjust the microphone into the precise position you want. It's also a good idea to take the musician into your confidence, explaining why you are positioning the microphone the way you are and just what sort of results you are trying to achieve. You can, for example, get a sound-swelling effect by having the musician move his instrument back and forth in the microphone area. Also, the musician can accentuate certain tones for emphasis by bringing his instrument close to the microphone at times, and a de-emphasis by moving it away. In this way the electronics becomes part of the musician's technique. With the help of the microphone, the musician can get sounds he could not possibly obtain by playing without microphone pickup.

The frequency response of the microphone will have an effect on banjo or guitar results. If you use a microphone with a frequency response rise somewhere around 1 kHz or 2 kHz you will find the music sounding more brilliant.

ACOUSTIC GUITAR

The acoustic guitar is another of those instruments whose sound output is delicate and whose volume output is so low that its tones can easily be lost among more "pushy" instruments.

Some recordists like to emphasize the sound made by the fingers along the guitar strings, with strong arguments in favor of realism. Others regard such sounds as intrusive. While you will have maximum natural pickup by "firing" the microphone directly at the guitar's center hole, playback of the tape may indicate this isn't quite what you want.

In general, you can record the acoustic guitar by putting a microphone behind the bridge, placing the microphone over the neck of the guitar at the point where it joins the guitar body, or by aiming the microphone at the hole of the guitar. An omni or two way microphone supplies natural bass. Miking in close with a cardioid exaggerates the bass. Figure 6-8 shows a method of recording the acoustic guitar with a contact microphone.

How Many Mikes Per Instrument?

The usual concept in recording the acoustic guitar is to consider just a single microphone. However, it is possible to

Fig. 6-8. Recording the acoustic guitar with a contact microphone.

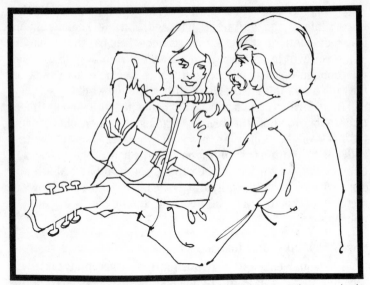

Fig. 6-9. Vocalist with two-guitar accompaniment, using a single microphone.

use two or three mikes, depending entirely on the kind of results you want to achieve.

Thus, in Fig. 6-9 we have a vocalist with a two-guitar accompaniment. The vocal is the important part of the composition and the microphone is positioned to pick up the voice of the singer. The mike will also pick up guitar sound, but to a lesser extent. In this example, the softness of the guitar accompaniment is somewhat overcome by using two instruments.

Figure 6-10 shows a solo vocalist with guitar accompaniment, but using two microphones, with one mike aimed at the hole of the guitar, the other at the singer's mouth. In this arrangement the performer has greater control over the sound. There is no loss of guitar background when the vocalist stops singing. With this setup the performer has a better choice of vocal solo, guitar solo, or a combination of both.

A lot depends on whether you are recording a solo guitar or a guitar plus accompaniment. If it is guitar with accompaniment you'll need to do much more experimenting to get the sound you want.

It is also true that what you get on tape will depend greatly on the musician, his expertise, and the instrument he is using.

But the best musician and the finest instrument cannot overcome the way in which the recording is made. If you have prior recording experience, fine. If not, experiment.

Acoustic vs. Electric Guitars

Guitars can be acoustic or amplified. The acoustic guitar has a larger body than that of the electric guitar and a strong sound is provided by the resonance of the instrument. The guitar recording techniques mentioned earlier are just a few of the many that are possible. If you mount an omni about a foot from the circular opening of the guitar you will get a good blend of guitar sound and the atttack of the guitarist plucking the strings. However, if you are planning to use a cardioid, be careful, since proximity effect can result in an unnatural coloration of the guitar sound. A condenser microphone provides exciting clarity and detail for acoustical guitar performance. You can also get a special microphone contact device, such as the AKG D-140, specifically designed for the acoustical classical guitar, useful in providing microphone separation when recording a singing guitarist. You can record

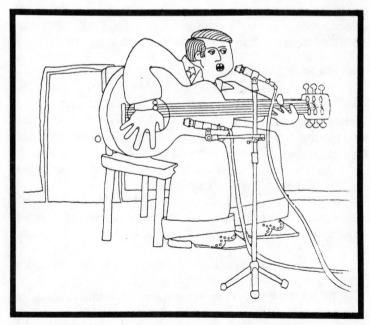

Fig. 6-10. Two microphone method for recording vocalist with guitar accompaniment.

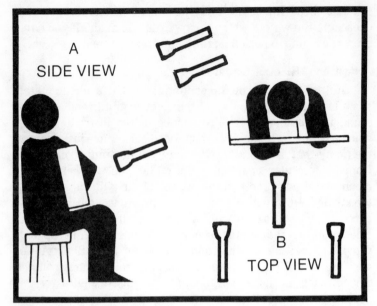

Fig. 6-11. Three microphone technique for guitar soloist. Side view (A) and top view (B).

an electric guitar in a manner similar to that in recording the electric bass, using a microphone in front of the guitar amplifier's cone speaker or via a transformer-type direct box.

Three-Mike Technique for Recording the Acoustic Guitar

You can use three mikes to record the guitar, with the main mike, a cardioid, close in to the instrument, and a microphone pair further away (Fig. 6-11). If the main microphone is too close, you may pick up the sounds of the fingers as they attack the strings or slide along the frets. To some listeners such sounds are annoying; to others they supply realism. It is entirely subjective.

Room acoustics will also influence the kind of sound you get, with the positioning of the microphone pair being influenced by the "liveliness" or "deadness" of the recording room.

The spot microphone (Fig. 6-11) must be delicately adjusted. Gain from this microphone must be spare. Always work in the 'little' direction since spot overemphasis can wipe out stereo effect.

The positioning of the single microphone will be influenced by the composition to be played. Grace notes on the guitar, while beautiful, can be much quieter than plucked notes, and so you may need to microphone in closer than you would ordinarily.

THE ELECTRIC GUITAR

The music from the electric guitar doesn't come from the instrument but, rather, from the speaker connected to the guitar amplifier. What we have, in effect, is double amplification. The electric guitar has a built-in transducer—a microphone—which develops an electrical signal which is then fed into the guitar amplifier. The output of the guitar amplifier is connected to a speaker. The amplifier isn't necessarily a high-fidelity unit. Sometimes distortion is deliberately introduced to obtain certain wanted musical effects.

What you want to do, then, is to point the microphone at that part of the speaker that produces the loudest sound (See Fig. 6-12). You can do this by disconnecting the input to the

Fig. 6-12. Recording the electric guitar.

microphone amplifier. Turn the microphone amplifier on, turn up the amplifier gain, and run a listening test on the speaker cone. Remove the grille cloth if there is one. You will hear a hissing sound coming from the speaker cone, but one part of the cone may seem to be supplying more hiss than any other part. Aim the microphone at this particular area.

With the acoustic guitar, the sound obtained is due to the kind of wood used in making the guitar, the shape and size of the guitar, and the kind of strings used. In the electric guitar, the quality or kind of sound is determined by the amplifier and speaker system. These should be regarded as an integral part of the guitar. That is why an electric guitar can sound so different when the musician uses the amplifier and speakers supplied by the hall in which he is going to play. Different amplifier + different speakers + different speaker enclosures = different sound.

One of the reasons for miking the electric guitar close in to the speaker box is to avoid picking up stage noises. You may not hear the shuffling of feet, or the pulling of cables along the stage floor, but the microphone will. However, if you are recording in your home you may not have these problems, or at least not to such a degree.

Sound output from a guitar speaker can blast the microphone and its following preamp. It is better to have the guitar amplifier gain turned down a bit and the microphone close in than to have the microphone farther away with the guitar amplifier gain turned up more.

BOWED STRING INSTRUMENTS

Violins and violas have resonant bodies which produce a combination of rich harmonic structure combined with the high-frequency harshness of the bowing action. A cardioid microphone placed to the violinist's side, aimed down from a boom slightly to the side of the bow, will give a rich sound with minimum harshness, depending on side placement.

THE ORGAN

Pipe and electronic organs, as used in churches and theatres, produce a sound in which the room housing the instrument plays an important part in the tonal color of the instrument. Pipe organs produce more mechanical noises nearest the pipes, but some of that noise and the air noise adds to the character and distinction of the instrument.

Use several microphones when making an organ recording. Close placement of a cardioid microphone to the instrument pipes or speakers will capture the high-frequency detail and the percussive effect of the instrument. (See Fig. 6-13.) Another omni or cardioid microphone placed in the room will provide the room ambience and reverberation which gives body to the organ sound.

If the organ is in a church you will find that the church altar makes an excellent microphone positioning point for reverberant sound.

For three-microphone pickup of organ sound, position the stereo mikes so as to pick up direct sound from the organ pipes, but put them close enough to obtain the harmonics. The sound level will depend on a number of variable factors: the music being played, the technique of the organist, the type of organ, and the acoustic environment. The two stereo mikes will be the main pickup units; the third mike, facing the alter, is intended to pick up broadly reverberent sounds.

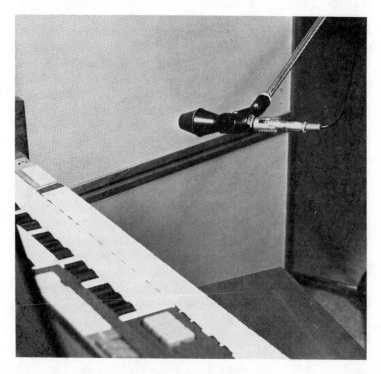

Fig. 6-13. Recording the electronic organ.

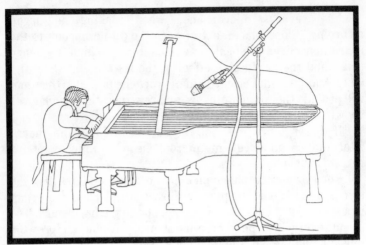

Fig. 6-14. Microphone pickup of grand piano.

THE PIANO

There are many ways of recording the piano. For a grand piano (Fig. 6-14) or upright, raise the lid on the grand and lift it or remove it from the upright. In the case of the spinet, use a cardioid and put it two thirds the way to the upper register facing down into the mechanism from a boom arm suspended 6 to 12 inches above the opening. This positioning will give a good balance of low and high frequencies. Be careful that proximity effect doesn't add too much coloration to the sound. You'll get the balance of piano attack and tonal resonance you want by raising or lowering the height of the microphone.

There are various techniques recordists use for the grand piano. One is to put the microphone near the hammers, selecting a spot near *middle C*. If you want to emphasize the bass of a particular composition, position the mike toward the rear of the piano in the bass string section. With the piano lid open, and using a cardioid, aim the microphone into the piano. Piano sound is reflected from the bottom of the open piano lid and you also get direct sound from the points where the hammers hit the strings. Work between the strings and the bottom of the lid until you record the kind of piano sound you prefer. A two-way cardioid can be particularly responsive to string harmonics.

Upright Piano

For the upright piano, there are three general techniques you can try. You can put a microphone over the open top of the piano, inside it, or behind the sound board.

Placement and blending can provide a wide panorama of piano sound, but remember that people don't only hear music on playback, they also get a mental image of the instrument. You may like the sound when reproduced; but if you generate a vision of an 8 foot wide piano, the microphone positioning technique is unrealistic.

Depending on room acoustics and microphone separation of instruments near the piano, you can place a cardioid microphone close for distinctively sharp piano sound or farther away for better tonal blending. Generally, a single microphone placed in the middle of the piano's arc, aimed down at the strings, will give a good tonal blend. For pop recording where close placement is customary, a single microphone aimed down at the second hole from the keyboard will give the necessary balance. When recording a piano-playing vocalist (Fig. 6-15), correct placement will ensure separation of the vocal signal from that of the piano for best mixing and control.

Three-Mike Technique for Recording the Piano

Put one cardioid mike close to the piano. The piano is a percussive instrument and the sharp rise and fall times of the

Fig. 6-15. Microphone placement for vocalist with piano accompaniment.

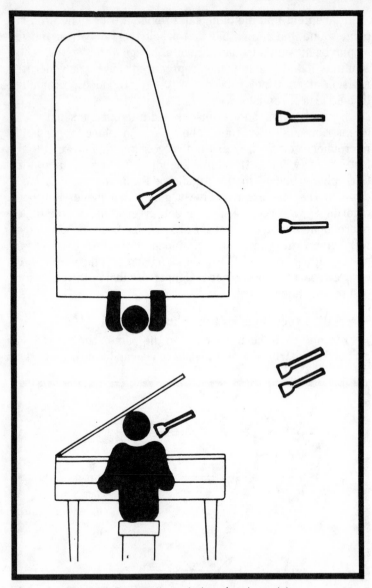

Fig. 6-16. Three-mike technique for piano pickup.

notes are the beauty of this string instrument. The distinctiveness of the percussive action decreases with distance from the instrument. Do not, however, have the microphone so close that it favors certain strings. The idea is to give equal pickup value to all the strings.

There is no absolute formula you can use for working distance, since not all musical compositions use the keyboard equally. Some compositions, for example, emphasize bass tones. Since the strings for bass tones produce more acoustic energy, you will need to position the single microphone a bit further away from the strings. If the composition emphasizes treble, move closer in.

Boom-mount the other two omni mikes (Fig. 6-16) for sound pickup six feet or so above ground and at least three feet apart. Precise positioning depends on the acoustics of the room. Generally, the larger the room the greater the distance of the mikes from the piano.

THE TYMPANI

This is a percussive instrument characterized by sudden starts having a high sound pressure level. Position the microphone 8 to 12 feet away and sufficiently high enough to clear the other instruments to get clear tympani sound.

THE CELLO AND BASS FIDDLE

If you want a sound characterized by brightness, position the mike over the bridge. For a full sound of either of these instruments, aim the microphone into the *F* hole. Experiment with positioning to minimize the sound of bow rasping. At the same time, try to get bass reproduction that is clear and distinctive, not muddy.

ORCHESTRAL BELLS, XYLOPHONE, VIBES

Mount the mike about four to six feet above the keyboard. Then adjust the mike for the best balance of sound with other instruments. Figure 6-17 shows alternative miking method.

PERCUSSION INSTRUMENTS IN GENERAL

Experiment with positioning of the microphone between two to six feet away from the instrument.

HORNS

Try positioning the microphone two to three feet from the bell to get the full sound of the instrument. You can mike closer in to the instrument, but if you get too close you will hear wind noise.

Fig. 6-17. Recording the xylophone.

THE VIOLIN

The cardioid response pattern should be smooth for linear off-axis response without coloration. Try positioning the microphone about two feet above the violin and direct it down into the hole. You'll find more freedom of movement without change of violin timbre because of any distance differential. (Fig. 6-18).

The cardioid pattern should be so smooth that the microphone will respond without tonal coloration when the violin is moved off axis.

STRING QUARTETS

Unlike the vocal quartet, the string quartet (Fig. 6-19) is usually arranged in the form of a semicircle. Visualize the performers located on the outer circumference of this circle with the sound directed toward the center. The center would then be the logical position of the main pickup microphone. If

Fig. 6-18. Recording the violin.

Fig. 6-19. Two-microphone pickup of a string quartet.

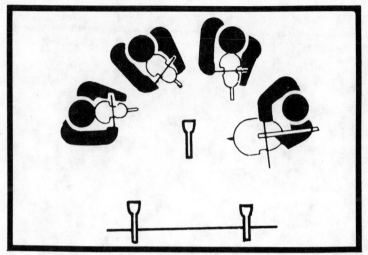

Fig. 6-20. Three-mike technique for recording a string quartet.

you prefer just one microphone and want to minimize audience noise pickup, use a cardioid. (Fig. 6-20). Some recordists, though, feel that audience noise adds realism. While the omni would seem to be a logical choice, either an omni or cardioid can be used. It is the spacing of the microphone from the group that makes the difference.

Not all instruments in a quartet produce the same sound level. If you have a problem of instrumental music balance, move the mike closer to the instrument whose sound must be brought up. Mount the microphone on a boom so it is above the heads of the players. Point the microphone downward so the head of the mike faces the instruments, as shown earlier in Fig. 6-19.

If you want to add a stereo effect (Fig. 6-20) use a pair of mikes located behind the main pickup unit, somewhat higher, and at least three feet from the nearest musician. Since it is a single, the main pickup microphone is mono; the separated pair are stereo. If the output level of the main pickup is too high, the effect on playback will be monophonic phase distortion and bad stereo. A good starting point is to have the output level of the mono and stereo mikes about the same and then to adjust the level down until you get the balance you prefer.

While professional string-quartet musicians often insist that string reproduction must be pure, some prefer a slightly attenuated bass response. They've found that diminished bass plus a very slight rise in both upper midrange and higher frequencies adds an instrumental presence that helps project a more forward string sound. Both microphones in a two microphone situation can be stand-mounted via a stereo bar or may be hung from the yoke of a stereo bar between 10 to 15 feet above the floor level. Angle the mikes down at the musicians at about an angle of 45°.

VIOLIN SOLO WITH PIANO ACCOMPANIMENT

Since violinists do not remain in one spot when playing, use an omni, positioning it at a height of about one to three feet above the violinist and about two to three feet in front. Do not set the microphone so that it is either horizontal or perpendicular to the violin strings, but select a position that is somewhere in between.

You can use a pair of stereo microphones to pick up reverberant sounds. Position these two mikes (Fig. 6-21) equidistant from the performer and at a greater distance than the single-pickup microphone, but the exact distance depends on the size of the room and its acoustics. You'll need to do some experimenting to get the best position that offers ideal balance between direct and reverberant sound.

Fig. 6-21. Recording the violin with piano accompaniment.

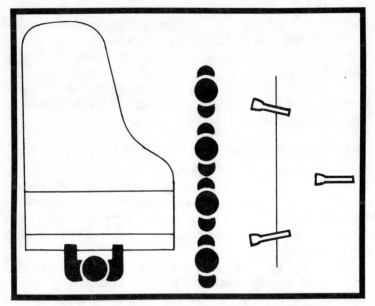

Fig. 6-22. Recording a quartet with piano accompaniment.

VOCAL QUARTET WITH PIANO ACCOMPANIMENT

Unlike the barbershop quartet usually clustered around the mike, the vocal quartet with a piano accompaniment is usually arranged as a single horizontal group in front of the piano. (Fig. 6-22). Further, the barbershop quartet usually huddles in closely, forming a rather tight group while the instrument-accompanied quartet tends to spread out. This requires greater microphone coverage and you should use at least two mikes. Mount the microphones just above the heads of the vocalists, but not too closely. The mikes should be wind-screen-equipped to minimize popping and blasting sounds.

JAZZ TRIO

A jazz trio will often consist of a piano, bass strings, and a set of drums. As in the case of the string quartet, the trio is arranged around a centrally positioned mike (Fig. 6-23). The microphone should be high enough so it is above the cymbals of the drum set. Start with the microphone positioned as centrally as possible, but you will probably find it quite off center when you are finished experimenting. Moving nearer to the drum set will emphasize the rhythm, but if you bring it too close the beat will override the musical theme supplied by the piano. If you locate the microphone too close to the bass strings you may get a thumping effect. Some recordists start with the microphone near the drum set and then gradually move the microphone back for the best sound balance.

If you want to include the acoustics of the room in the recording or you want to supply stereo, mount a pair of mikes higher than the main pickup and farther back. All mikes should point downward toward the performers. You might also try beginning with the main pickup mike, working back and forth with it until you get the kind of sound you want. This sound will be mono. Then add a stereo pair and adjust their position with respect to the main pickup mike until you get the kind of balance between the main and stereo pair you want. The idea here is to fix the position of the main pickup first and then find the best position of the stereo mikes. If you try to adjust all three mikes simultaneously you may find yourself frustrated by the enormous number of possibilities.

SCHOOL BAND ON STAGE

To capture the full sound of an orchestra, professional people are inclined to use two wide-range full-frequency cardioids. Each cardioid is approximately one-third in from the end of the orchestra for wide panoramic sound.

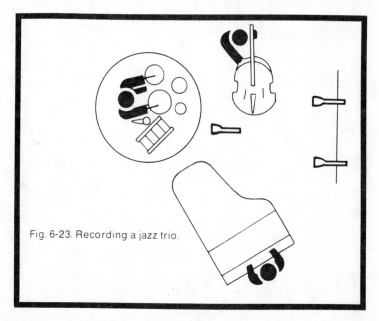

Fig. 6-23. Recording a jazz trio.

Chapter 7
How to Use
Microphones: Voices

HOW TO USE MICROPHONES: VOICES

Continuing our discussion concerning microphone applications and techniques, this chapter will discuss the use of microphones when recording vocals, both solo and group, and voices with musical accompaniment.

RECORDING THE SOLO VOCALIST

There is no such thing as a single, universal microphone suitable for all solo vocalists. The type of microphone to use depends on the performer and the type of singing. For example, a rock performer usually works his microphone as hard as he works himself, and such singers have special problems. The fact is that no matter how hard a microphone is worked, it must have a clean, linear response with balanced bass reproduction, even when used close to the mouth (Fig. 7-1). Because of the high sound pressure levels of rock program material, proximity effect, usually associated with cardioids, must be limited. While the microphone may be designed for very high sound pressure levels, it should respond well under overload conditions and effectively reject low-frequency sounds that result in feedback.

Also, because of the nature of rock music, such performers may want to consider a microphone that delivers a more brilliant sound. Such a microphone tends to increase intelligibility and allow a more forward vocal projection.

Rock singers are active singers and not every microphone is made to take the punishment. Microphones should have a transducer element that is elastically shock-mounted to resist

Fig. 7-1. Recording the solo vocalist. Performer working microphone close in.

any response to external microphone or cable vibrations. The performer, no matter how active, needs complete freedom of movement.

Of course, not all vocalists are rock singers. There are all sorts. Some people just like to sing. And while they're singing, they like to move around a little. The trouble is that while they're moving, the microphone is standing still, and that can be a problem.

When the performer must have room to move, most likely he will be about two to three feet from the microphone. The customary thing to do to reach a natural sound level is to boost amplification. But higher amplification means possible feedback problems.

In such situations, you should consider a microphone that is comparatively free from bass coloration. Otherwise, as with many cardioid microphones, bass overemphasis will occur when the microphone is worked too closely, and vocal timbre will change as the performer moves toward and away from the microphone.

For this soloist, consider a two-way double-element cardioid microphone with an extremely wide frequency response. The microphone should have an extremely flat off-axis rejection—it should reject different sound frequencies equally without discrimination to allow for considerably higher volume levels before feedback.

Finally, the closer the microphone is to the mouth of the vocalist, the greater the chance of recording *aspiration*, the sound of the vocalist's breathing. This usually happens when the microphone is about one inch from the mouth of the performer. All it takes is a few more inches of working distance to eliminate breathing sounds.

For solo vocalists the hand-held cardioid is best. The relative closeness of the mike to the mouth supplies a higher signal-to-noise ratio—that is, there is less opportunity for ambient noise to get at the mike. The hand-held mike also provides better separation and control between the vocals and accompanying instruments. A mike with a three-position *mode* switch is useful in reducing bass response. The idea here is to supply more vocal brilliance against an instrumental background.

Single element cardioid dynamics are more directional at high frequencies than omnis. If you are miking a vocalist or instrumentalist you can get more sharply defined high-frequency response by pointing the microphone right at the performer's instrument or at the mouth of the vocalist. Conversely, if you want to reduce high-frequency crispness, point the microphone upward or to one side.

Vocalists should try singing over the top of the microphone or slightly off to one side. When using cardioid microphones you'll find that you won't pop your p's this way. T's, sibilants and breath sounds will also sound better.

With cardioids, vary the distance between mouth and microphone. When singing loudly, move the head back slightly, or move the microphone away. When a soft, intimate mood sound is needed, bring the microphone closer to the mouth.

Close-Up Vocals

There are a number of problems associated with close-up vocals. With a loud orchestra, or even with a loud succession of musical passages, the vocalist may try to overcome the background and the result may be pre-amplifier input overload distortion. *Overload distortion* is a condition that, in this instance, is produced when the output voltage of the microphone is larger than the permitted input signal voltage level of the preamplifier which follows the microphone.

With the microphone placed so close to the lips of the vocalist, it may produce breath pop. Some of the mouthed sounds, such as words using the letters p or t, are percussive. Also, with a hand-held microphone there is always the possibility of producing mechanical noise.

A windscreen will prevent breath pop and, of course, is necessary for outdoor use. The amount of *microphone handling noise*—mechanical noise—is a function of the construction of the mike. This is one of the features you don't see when you buy a microphone, but is something you should ask about when you do.

Distant Vocals

Not all vocalists enjoy holding a microphone, for a number of reasons. Some feel that the presence of the microphone hides part of the face, and for a vocalist trying to achieve personality projection, this can be a serious consideration. If a vocalist is really capable of "belting it out" the presence of the microphone implies that his or her voice requires an electrical assist, when this may not be the case at all. Also, the vocalist may be occupied with playing an instrument while singing, and a hand-held mike cannot be considered.

You can compensate for the fact that the microphone is now more than six inches away from the artist by turning up the gain of the preamp. This isn't an unmixed blessing, for when you do you also raise the level of background noise. You may also introduce a condition of feedback (consisting of sound returned by the speakers to the mike) making the amplifier less stable than it should be. At its worst, feedback can produce howling, an extreme case. More subtly, feedback can raise the gain of the amplifier over a limited frequency range, giving tones that come within that range a sharpness they shouldn't have. The microphone is also capable of picking up sound reflected from the stage floor or hard walls behind the vocalist. This can change the character of the sound going into the microphone.

With the microphone removed from the performer, one problem, that of breath pop, is automatically eliminated. The microphone that is needed in this situation is one that has a pickup pattern so that the microphone is most responsive to sounds coming at it from the front and insensitive to sounds reaching the microphone from all other directions. This means, then, that the microphone should have a cardioid pickup characteristic. Feedback will be much less critical; but if it persists, try moving the speakers to a different location, or, if that isn't possible, move the vocalist to a new spot.

Vocalist With Piano Accompaniment

Whenever you have a vocalist with instrument accompaniment there is always the possibility that the instrument will override the vocalist. This may force the vocalist (Fig. 7-2) to shorten the working distance in an effort to increase the vocal sound level. Recording, however, should never be a contest. Listen carefully to the balance between the instrument and vocal and adjust the instrument level accordingly. As a general rule, instrument level should never rise to more than 50 percent of vocal level. Of course, there's always the possibility that you will make the instrument level much too high compared to vocal and background levels. This will tend to make the recording sound monophonic. The listener on playback should be able to visualize the location of the vocalist with respect to the accompaniment. If the vocalist is too loud compared to the instrument it will appear, on playback, that there is a considerable distance between the two performers. If the instrument is louder than the vocalist, it will seem as though the piano is right up against the vocalist.

When recording a vocalist accompanied by a piano there is a natural tendency to concentrate on the two performers and to ignore the acoustics of the auditorium. Reverberant sound and audience noise do contribute substantially to realism. You can use a pair of omnis, located away from the main pickup microphone and more toward the audience, as shown in Fig. 7-3. The main microphone, a cardioid, will be more sensitive to the percussive effects of both voice and piano, while the omnis will add a sense of spaciousness to the sound.

THE BARBERSHOP QUARTET

Because harmony is a blend of separate voices, usually in different keys, each voice must retain its own particular vocal characteristics if harmony is to be maintained at audience level. If the balance of the voices is upset, the result can be quite the opposite of harmony. It's important, then, for such a group to consider a microphone with a linear response across

Fig. 7-2. Vocalist with piano accompaniment.

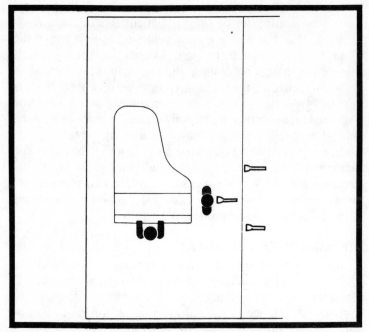

Fig. 7-3. Three-microphone method for recording a solo vocalist with piano accompaniment.

the full frequency range, a microphone that responds cleanly and is free of coloration. Further, because such small groups tend to cluster around the microphone, it should respond well to voices that reach it off axis so that individual vocal timbre is maintained.

GOSPEL, FOLK, AND COUNTRY VOCAL GROUP

Use omnis or cardioids for best off-axis pickup fidelity of vocalists to the sides of the microphone. Make A−B separation at least three feet. Microphone X − Y (explained on page 185) on the stereo bar with cardioids only.

You'll probably find that the two-way cardioid is best for effective recording of a group vocal. This microphone supplies a more uniform response over a wider acceptance angle than you can get with single-element microphones.

THE POP GROUP

Use a cardioid for the vocal, an omni or cardioid for the drum set, and a cardioid for the kick drum. For additional instruments use a cardioid or omni.

Keep all microphones very close. You'll need booms to give the performers play room. Use a microphone mixer to control sound balance and add microphone attenuation pads if the mixer input produces distortion. That's quite likely, particularly if the group lets itself go. Use a close microphone setup for feedback control in sound reinforcement.

COUNTRY AND WESTERN GROUPS

Use a cardioid pair with left and right A−B stereo spacing. Keep the mikes high and angled down. You will probably need to do some experimenting with microphone positioning. Start with the microphone stands several feet away from the group (Fig. 7-4). Moving the mikes closer to the band or farther away will control room sound and balance. Also, try both mikes in an X−Y configuration on the stereo bar with one stand in the center. Refer to page 185.

SMALL GROUPS, ORCHESTRAS, AND CHOIRS

The primary recording technique uses a left/right spaced microphone pair. This is described professionally as A−B time-intensity stereo. The stereo spread is created by the difference in arrival time and loudness from any source to both microphones.

Fig. 7-4. Microphone positioning for a country and western group.

Fig. 7-5. Two-microphone pickup of a small vocal group.

In this arrangement the multiple sound sources, such as small groups, orchestras, and choirs, are progressively left and right, closer to one or the other microphone (Fig. 7-5). The closer microphone collects the sound quicker and louder than the more remote microphone. The same precedence is perceived during playback and recreates the feeling of spacious, horizontal stereo spread.

ROCK GROUPS

In this recording situation, each instrument and the vocalist, if any, all try to outdo each other. Maximum loudness is the order of the day. The only practical solution seems to be to use a microphone for each instrument, with a separate boom or stand for the vocalist recording. Use cardioids. You'll need to mike in closely to keep any one instrument from being overwhelmed.

If a guitar is used in this group it will be an electric, sometimes working into a fuzz box. A *fuzz box* is an amplifier deliberately designed to distort sound or produce unusual sound effects. While some rock music seems to be an exercise in noise production, some is highly musical and beautiful. Listening to rock music is a subjective experience, as it is with all other music.

If you have never recorded before, starting with rock is an extremely ambitious undertaking, not only for the multiplicity of microphones involved, but simply because rock recording requires at least a measure of professionalism. However, if you can record rock and can produce acceptable playback, you can consider yourself to have graduated in the school of microphone use.

Figure 7-6. shows some of the ways to record rock. If you have a pair of electronic amplifiers, try to separate them widely and arrange for microphone pickup by having one cardioid for each, facing in to the cones of the speakers. For the drum set, mount one or two mikes on stands, with the mike heads facing fown but still out of the reach of any upward moving drum stick. Of course, all the mikes have to be working in phase.

RECORDING LARGE GROUP, ORCHESTRA, OR CHOIR

There is a simple approach to spacing a left/right microphone pair in front of a large orchestra or choir (Fig. 7-7). Stand on a center line facing the musical group. With the performers in action, move backward and forward, closer and farther away until you like the live sounds as a listener. From this preferred listening position, extend imaginary sight lines angling to the left and right edges of the performers.

You are now at the apex of a triangle. The musical group in front of you is the base. Put the left and right microphones on each angled sight line an equal distance from the base. The left to right spacing of the microphones, at the start, can be equal to one half the distance between yourself and the base line.

This is your basic starting setup. Now move the two microphones closer to or farther from the base line so you can control room reverberation. You can change the left/right microphone spacing to adjust stereo perspective. Keep in mind that the left/right microphones should be closer rather than further apart to avoid having a hole in center sound reproduction.

Each microphone should be equally as high as possible on fully extended floor stands. Use microphone boom arms on the floor stands for even more height. Highly placed microphones angling downward help establish the loudness balance between the front and last rows of the performing group. Final

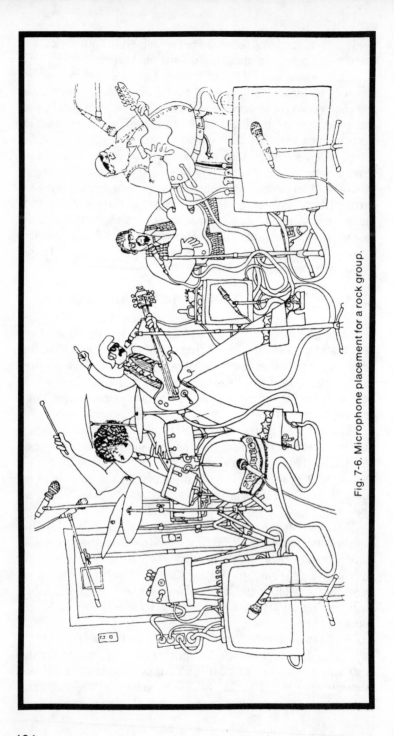

Fig. 7-6. Microphone placement for a rock group.

positioning is achieved when balance and stereo perspective are acceptable on subjective playback evaluation tests.

There is also a less known, but remarkably effective stereo recording technique known as X—Y intensity stereo. The microphone pair (cardioids) is mounted on a stereo bar with the heads almost touching, as shown in the small insert in Fig. 7-7, and crossfiring left and right from one coincident position. Separate microphone tails from 90° to 120°, depending on the kind of group you are miking—that is, whether they are a narrow or wide group. Use on a boom, high in the center, several feet from the group.

When using the X—Y intensity stereo technique remember to reverse connections to your tape recorder input, since the right-position microphone covers the left side of the performing group, and vice versa.

You can also use an omni pair spaced for A—B stereo mounted on booms and shock absorbing stands. Try the mikes one-third the group width apart and several feet down in front. Mount the mikes as high as possible and angle them down to the last rows of performers. If reverberation is excessive, move the omnis closer to the group or else switch to cardioids.

Fig. 7-7. Microphone placement for large vocal group. Inset (lower right) shows arrangement of X—Y cross cardioids.

Microphone pairs for spaced and coincident stereo sound collection should be identical models and have the same pickup patterns. If you use microphones that are different and whose frequency responses and pickup patterns aren't the same, you can get an unbalanced, disoriented stereo image in playback. The sound sources will not relocate correctly in playback and can swim back and forth in the stereo image.

You can use an omini pair or a cardioid pair. However, use only a cardioid pair for coincident stereo bar mounting, since only directional microphones will be most effective. When all sound sources are an equal distance from the two microphones, virtually in the same place, there will be no difference in arrival time, only changes in loudness.

The setup suggested here for music group recording requires a simple mixer for individual microphone level control and final balance in the recording. You can use the same setup for sound reinforcement.

The exact technique in recording large orchestras or choirs will largely depend on the size of the group, the size of the room, and its acoustics. If the room isn't excessively reverberant, a combination of direct sound and room reverberance will add warmth and body to the recording.

The problem of recording a church choir with organ is not so much in getting good sound but in getting too much low frequency organ sound. Here you should consider the advantage of a microphone designed to roll off slightly in the bass region. Low-end response would sound more natural, an advantage in reverberant situations. At the same time, a gradual, slight rise in the upper midrange and high frequencies would add vocal presence.

RECORDING A CHOIR OR SMALL CHILDREN

Use a cardioid pair mounted on a stereo bar. With one boom and a stand you can position the microphones centered and high, several feet from the choir. Separate the microphone tails from 90° to 120°, depending on the width of the group. Crossfire with the microphone heads almost touching.

If the choir has a solo singer, use a separate boom-mounted mike for this voice pickup. Start by recording the choir with the cardioid pair until you get the sound you want. Then bring in the soloist and adjust the soloist's microphone until you get the proper balance between soloist and choir.

Chapter 8
How to Use Microphones:
Special Applications

HOW TO USE MICROPHONES: SPECIAL APPLICATIONS

Once again continuing our discussion on how to use the microphone, this chapter covers application procedures and special techniques for using the microphone to capture the spoken word, whether it be a news conference, a speech, or a press conference—as well as recording *natural* sounds. There is also special information on ringing and howling and some final tips on using the microphone.

INTERVIEW AND CONFERENCE RECORDING

If you are recording an interview with one or more persons, an omni microphone or cardioid straight up in the middle of the group will supply the most uniform recording with noncritical microphone placement. This setup can be used for recordings made at a conference table.

If the recording is being made in a high ambient noise environment, cardioid mikes can help because of their discrimination against unwanted sounds. Sometimes a stereo recording with two cardioids will provide better speech intelligibility. The directionality of the cardioid helps in speaker identification. If the environment is highly reverberant, a number of mikes may be needed to lessen speaker to microphone distance for best clarity.

MICROPHONES AT THE PODIUM

Whether for lectures in an auditorium or church pulpit, microphone placement at the podium can provide the key to successful communications between a lecturer and his audience. Because single-element cardioids characteristically have good on-axis response with reduced high-frequency response off axis, two such microphones are often used on a podium to provide a wider coverage area, particularly if the lecturer has a tendency to move around. Two microphones placed at opposite corners of the podium and aimed at the lecturer provide variations in response when the lecturer moves from one side of the podium to the other. A better placement of the two microphones is in the middle of the podium, with the microphones aimed so that their heads touch at a 90° angle. Wider pickup coverage of the lecturer is provided without phase cancellation.

If one microphone is used, a two-way cardioid placed in the center of the podium provides much better coverage than a single-element unit. If the microphone is placed in front of the system's loudspeakers, it may be necessary to put the microphone on a gooseneck to bring the microphone-to-subject distance closer and reduce acoustic feedback. In selecting a microphone for this use, choose one that has wide pickup angle and a switchable bass attenuator. This feature will provide further control of acoustic feedback.

LECTURE RECORDING

A lecturer seated at a desk can be troubled by reflection of sound from the desk top. If the microphone is 12 or more inches from the lecturer and is placed on a desk stand, tabletop reflections can cause phase cancellations and affect sound quality.

In reinforcing or recording conferences you may need to use a number of microphones to get adequate pickup. Excessive room reverberation is a common problem as more microphones are used. You can try out-of-phase pairs of microphones placed back to back.

RECORDING WITH HAND-HELD MICROPHONES

For hand-held use, reduced bass response below 150 Hz is desirable to minimize handling noise and proximity effect. Microphones designed for recording, as well as hand-held use, often have a recessed bass attenuator switch in the microphone shaft. Extended bass is provided in the flat position of the switch and bass attenuation at the other switch position.

Two-way cardioid microphones, with their extended bass response, are not generally recommended for hand-held use. Performers often like the proximity effect of the single-element cardioid. When close-talked the increased output lessens feedback and provides better separation of vocals from instruments. Omnis require less critical placement by performers and do not have proximity effect, but you will get increased stage band pickup and there is always the possibility of quicker acoustic feedback.

ORCHESTRA MICROPHONES

When using microphones to reinforce an orchestra located directly below the performer, place microphones so there is separation between orchestral and vocal sounds. If the orchestra is picked up by the vocalist's microphone, and vice versa, the sound-system operator will not be able to provide adequate separation and control of the sound sources.

GENERAL RECOMMENDATIONS
FOR SOUND-SYSTEM OPERATORS

The amount of amplification before feedback in a sound reinforcement system is generally dependent on the microphone, loudspeaker, and room acoustics. In a difficult feedback-prone environment, the minimum number of microphones live at any time will assure minimum acoustic feedback. The acoustic gain available before feedback is reduced by 3 dB each time the number of live microphones in use is doubled. Four live microphones will reduce acoustic gain by 6 dB as compared to one microphone.

When the sound system must be operated close to the feedback threshold, try using low-frequency filters, either in the microphone or tone controls in the amplifier. This will minimize feedback. You should always have plug-in attenuator pads for those situations in which the performer practically swallows the microphone.

FILM AND STAGE MICROPHONE APPLICATIONS

Often mounted on a boom, the shotgun microphone allows microphone pickup control over a narrow angle, as required. A common assumption, but a mistaken one, is that a shotgun microphone will produce exceptional results in a typically reverberant room. In such a room, sound emanating from the sides or rear of the microphone will reverberate from the front walls of the room and come in front of the shotgun.

When used on a boom to pick up an actor's voice, a shotgun microphone can also pick up sound reflections from the wall behind the actor, minimizing intelligibility of the actor's words. When used under proper techniques, indoors and outdoors, the shotgun microphone is a workhorse of the film, stage, and broadcast industry. In outdoor use, a foam windscreen will provide a wind noise reduction of about 20 dB. Shock-mount shotgun microphones to booms or other mounts to minimize handling and boom noise.

MICROPHONE PICKUP OF STAGE PERFORMANCES

Tabletops provide sound reflection that cause phase cancellation in microphone pickup of an announcer seated at a table. Stage floors provide similar reflections and, when footlight microphones are mounted on short pipes above the stage floor, phase cancellation can result in supplying the sound with a distance quality. Try putting microphones on thin foam pads on the stage floor instead. This will supply full sound quality without sound cancellation and with minimum mechanical transmission of foot noise. Single microphones placed at intervals across the stage apron or pairs of microphones crossfired at 90°, provide uniform sound pickup with minimum visibility.

MICROPHONE APPLICATIONS
FOR SOUND REINFORCEMENT

Microphone selection and placement for sound reinforcement applications adds another problem area— *acoustic feedback*. Generally, in a sound reinforcement arrangement, the microphone, loudspeaker system, and the room play equal parts in the successful or unsuccessful performance of the reinforcement system.

Acoustic feedback is caused when sound from the speaker system reaches the microphone at such intensity and phase relationship as to put the sound system into a condition of positive feedback. This results in a condition of oscillation or ringing. The sound fed back from the speakers to the microphone is in phase with the sound going into the microphone. The two, the *original* sound and the *reinforced* or *amplified* sound, strengthen each other and do so in a continuing process. If kept within limits, the result will be ringing, making the sound extremely sharp. If the feedback continues its growth, the result will be howling. In old-style telephone systems using a separate ear piece, pranksters sometimes achieved the same effect by holding the earpiece up to the mouthpiece of the telephone.

Sound feedback can occur in either a professional or home recording situation. Further, the ringing or howling will take place at a particular frequency or a small band of frequencies. You may find the condition occuring when a certain note is struck.

No two systems will feedback at the same frequency. A room has its fundamental and harmonic resonances, in addition to an amount of reverberation, that produce their effect on good sound. A microphone with a smooth frequency response on axis and uniform cancellation off axis can produce more amplification before feedback than can a microphone with peaky response and uneven cardioid rejection.

In use, the two-way cardioid microphone with its smooth on-axis response, smooth 90° response, and uniform back rejection at both high and low frequencies (as compared to many single-element cardioid microphones, which have good rejection at mid frequencies only) can provide up to 6 dB more amplification before feedback as compared to a similarly priced single-element cardioid microphone. Proximity effect, peaky high frequency response, and uneven back rejection cause acoustic feedback prevalent in so many sound reinforcement systems.

Cardioid microphones respond best to sounds directed toward the front of the microphone, with less pickup sensitivity to audience sounds and extraneous house noises that reach it from the rear. A well-designed cardioid mucrophone will reject most of the unwanted hall or auditorium reverberation effects, which, if amplified, can lead to feedback. One of the great advantages of the cardioid microphone is its inherent resistance to feedback problems, the squealing, howling sound that occurs when the amplified signal fed through the speaker system is picked up by the microphone and reamplified. Because cardioid microphones tend to reject speaker-generated sounds that reach the microphone from the rear, there is much less possibility of feedback and a higher level of amplification can be used.

RINGING AND HOWLING

Where you are working with a three-mike setup, using a pair of cardioids for stereo pickup and a third, more remote omni to supply background sounds for presence, the single omni located too close to speakers can result in feedback. Try turning the speakers into a different position and, if possible, facing them away from the omni. If you have obtained the correct sound balance between the stereo cardioids and the omni, try moving the speakers further away from the microphones. You may also need to turn the amplifier gain down a bit. Positive feedback not only requires a pair of in-phase audio signals into the microphone, but the sound from the speakers must be of sufficient amplitude to trigger the beginning of ringing or howling.

The fact that a sound reinforcement setup has ringing but no howling is no cause for satisfaction. The condition is a highly unstable one and it is possible that the slightest increase in sound strength of a particular tone will throw the sound system from ringing into howling. You can consider a sound reinforcement system as stable only if there is no evidence of ringing at any sound frequency, that is, no matter what tone is being played, no matter what combination of tones are being played, and no matter how loudly they are being played.

RECORDING OUTDOORS

If you plan to do any outdoor recording, a windscreen is absolutely essential. The usual windscreen supplied with a mike will serve in almost all applications, but there may be times when the windscreen is just not enough. In such cases, use a nylon stocking and wrap the microphone head with it. You may need to use one or more stocking layers.

RECORDING MOTION

When recording the sound made by a moving object, you can convey a sense of motion in the recording by using more than one microphone. Put a number of microphones along the path the object will take. Microphone separation will depend on the speed of the moving object. The faster it moves, the more widely spaced the mikes should be.

If you are recording a marching band, for example, position one microphone well ahead of the band to create the illusion of arrival. Other mikes, spaced at distances of about 50 feet, will help supply the image of a band in motion. You will heighten the effect by using cardioids. The crowd noise level will be rather high, and it is debatable whether you should also include an omni. If you do, keep close control of the background sound level so it does not override your primary objective—the sound of the marching band.

RECORDING NATURAL SOUNDS

You can record natural sounds in various ways. One is to use a parabola or "dish" that works as a *sound collector*. This is simply a large, dish-shaped metal reflector and is quite inexpensive. If you want to pick up bird sounds, arrange the microphones around the area where the birds normally gather. Use two or more cardioids, pointing inward to the feeding area. Stay in the distance to keep from frightening the birds and watch the action with binoculars.

You can use one or more microphones to collect all sorts of outdoors sounds. You can tape such sounds and then, if you have a tape deck that permits recording sound-with-sound, you can add such sounds to the sound of a vocalist, an instrumentalist, or an orchestra, to produce some unusual results. Many outdoor sounds have musical quality. Wind sounds, ordinary street noises, the movement of trains or cars, marching bands, and even crowd noises can sound quite unusual and interesting when recorded and played back in the quiet of your listening room.

RECORDING OFF THE AIR

You can record AM or FM broadcasts by positioning a mike or mikes somewhere in front of your speakers, but this isn't recommended. Even using cardioids, the mikes will pick up room noise or outdoor sounds. This is one instance in which you can eliminate the microphones and get better results. All you need do is to use a patch cord to connect your receiver's output to the input of your tape recorder. If your receiver isn't equipped with sound-signal output terminals on its rear apron, buy an earphone plug for connection to the earphone jack of the receiver. Use a pair of flexible wires to connect to the plug and attach the other end of these wires to the AUX or LINE input of your tape deck.

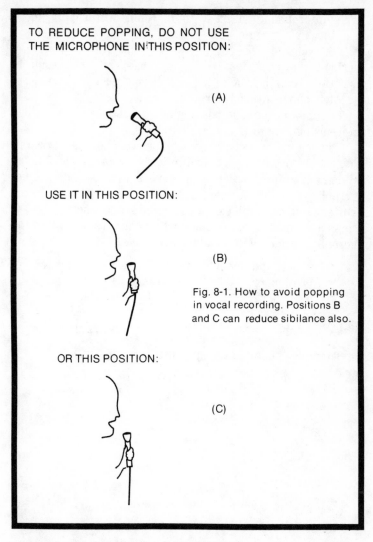

TO REDUCE POPPING, DO NOT USE
THE MICROPHONE IN THIS POSITION:

(A)

USE IT IN THIS POSITION:

(B)

Fig. 8-1. How to avoid popping
in vocal recording. Positions B
and C can reduce sibilance also.

OR THIS POSITION:

(C)

SOME FINAL TIPS ON MICROPHONES

Here are a few last minute suggestions for using microphones.

When using two mikes as a stereo pair, use the same model microphone made by the *same* manufacturer. Intermixing two different models in a stereo pair will make it difficult to obtain a correct stereo balance.

Remember that omnis pick up sound from all around and that cardioids favor front sound to rear sound.

A microphone stand with a boom will supply more flexibility in recording.

Very close-in use of the microphone means you may overload the recorder. When this happens, the result is distortion. Back off the mikes, but if you must work in close, use microphone attenuation pads.

Try the microphone positioning suggestions given earlier before using your own. *Experiment*.

The original sound source, whether vocal or instrumental, is direct or "dry" sound. Sound reflected from the walls, floor, ceiling, or other objects is reverberant sound. Adjust microphone spacing for best balance between the two.

Keep left/right mikes close to avoid a stereo hole.

As a general rule, or as a starting point, use the following microphone spacing for single instruments:

- strings and woodwinds   19 to 36 inches
- harmonica   9 to 12 inches
- accordion   19 to 36 inches
- brass   6½ feet
- vocals   19 to 20 inches

To reduce popping, see the illustrations in Fig. 8-1.

Chapter 9
Selecting the
Right Microphone

SELECTING THE RIGHT MICROPHONE

There are no fixed rules in choosing or applying to a microphone or microphones for recording applications. The microphone selection and placement recommendations given in the preceding pages are just a start. Results will depend on your own creativity, your patience, and your willingness to experiment. It will also be helpful if you have had some musical training. Also remember that the mikes you use in one recording environment may not necessarily be the best choice for another. The microphone positioning you have found to be suitable in one place isn't necessarily the way to record in another. However, the more you experiment with microphones and the more you learn about them, the more you will know about their behavior and their characteristics, and the greater will be your confidence in using them.

HOW TO SELECT A MICROPHONE
FOR DIFFERENT INSTRUMENTS

The chart in Fig. 9-1 is designed to supply you with a guide in your choice of AKG microphones for different instruments.

D-120 Series

Column A in Fig. 9-1 covers the D-120 series of AKG microphones. The cardioid pickup pattern is excellent for sound pickup without adding extraneous feedback. It is particularly suited for bass, bass drum, and electric guitar.

One advantage of microphones in the D-120 series is that they have a specially constructed diaphragm that can tolerate the high sound-pressure levels of hard-rock vocals. The D-120ES microphone comes complete with a built-in

SELECTING A MICROPHONE

	A	B	C	D	E
BRASS	●	●	X	●	X
REED	●	X	●	●	X
FOLK VOCAL	●	●	●	X	X
GOSPEL VOCAL	●	●	●	X	X
ROCK VOCAL	●	●	●	X	X
ACOUSTIC GUITAR	●	X	●	●	X
SNARE DRUM	●	●	X	●	X
BASS DRUM	X	●	●	●	X
CYMBAL	●	X		●	X
FLUTE	●	●	X	●	X
PICCOLO	●	X	●	●	X
ELECTRIC GUITAR	X	●	●	●	X
STRINGS	●	X	●	●	X
BASS	X	●	●	●	X
HARMONICA	●	●	X	●	X
PIANO	●	X	●	●	X

X PRIMARY CHOICE
● SECONDARY CHOICE

Fig. 9-1. Selection guide for microphones. See text for microphone types A through E.

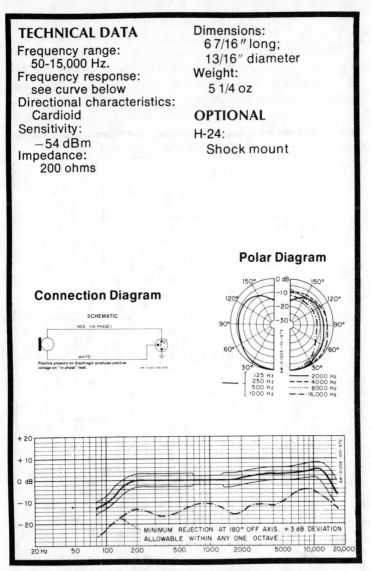

TECHNICAL DATA

Frequency range:
50-15,000 Hz.
Frequency response:
see curve below
Directional characteristics:
Cardioid
Sensitivity:
−54 dBm
Impedance:
200 ohms

Dimensions:
6 7/16 " long;
13/16" diameter
Weight:
5 1/4 oz

OPTIONAL

H-24:
Shock mount

Polar Diagram

Connection Diagram

SCHEMATIC

RED (IN PHASE)

WHITE

Positive pressure on diaphragm produces positive
voltage on "in phase" lead.

125 Hz
250 Hz
500 Hz
1000 Hz

2000 Hz
4000 Hz
8000 Hz
16,000 Hz

MINIMUM REJECTION AT 180° OFF AXIS. +3 dB DEVIATION
ALLOWABLE WITHIN ANY ONE OCTAVE.

Fig. 9-2. Technical data for AKG microphones, D-120 series.

on/off switch, a stand adaptor, and a padded carrying case.
You can use both high- and low-impedance cables for in the
D-120 series. Technical features for the D-120 series of AKG
microphones are shown in Fig. 9-2.

In the frequency response graph of the D-120 line, and
those in the following illustrations for other AKG lines, is the

response of the microphone within its acceptance range. The single line-frequency response curve at the bottom is the response of the microphone to sounds that are 180° off axis.

Column B in Fig. 9-1 represents the D-190 series, particularly suitable for use with reed instruments, the acoustic guitar, the piccolo, string instruments, the piano, and cymbals. A cardioid microphone, is intended for handling hard rock and is capable of working with very high sound-pressure levels without distorting. However, the sensitivity of microphones in this line is such that they are also responsive to muted tones. These mikes have a smooth response over the entire frequency range, without so-called "peaks" or "valleys". The D-190ES microphone comes complete with a built-in on/off switch, a stand adapter, and a padded carrying case. Both low- and high-impedance cables may be used with the D-190 series.

Technical features of the D-190 series are shown in Fig. 9-3.

Column C in Fig. 9-1 represents the D-1000, a practical choice for the working performer. It is particularly designed for the rugged abuse a microphone must take when musicians "take to the road." This microphone has a heavy-duty screen to prevent disturbing wind and breath noises.

Although it is a heavy-duty type, the D-1000 microphone is unusually sensitive. It has an extended low-end frequency response. And if you want to hear how it responds to treble sounds, try it with pure flute tones. The directional pickup pattern keeps feedback down no matter how loud the sound. The microphone comes complete with a built-in equalization switch, a stand adapter, and a padded carrying case. Both low- and high-impedance cables may be used.

Technical features of the D-1000 are shown in Fig. 9-4.

Column D in Fig. 9-1 represents the D-2000. Specifically made for use with vocals, it is capable of drlivering every sound detail, It has a built-in bass roll-off switch that lets the performer control sound while the microphone is in use. It alters the bass frequency to fit each performer's particular style. The switch supplies a selection of heavy bass (proximity effect) or normal bass. And the extended frequency range covers every subtle tone and overtone.

The D-2000 has a wide front-to-back pickup discimination that won't permit feedback. A built-in windscreen prevents

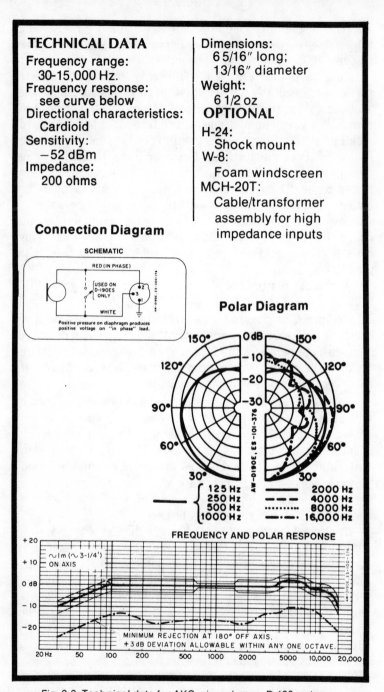

TECHNICAL DATA
Frequency range:
30-15,000 Hz.
Frequency response:
see curve below
Directional characteristics:
Cardioid
Sensitivity:
−52 dBm
Impedance:
200 ohms

Dimensions:
6 5/16" long;
13/16" diameter
Weight:
6 1/2 oz
OPTIONAL
H-24:
Shock mount
W-8:
Foam windscreen
MCH-20T:
Cable/transformer
assembly for high
impedance inputs

Connection Diagram

SCHEMATIC

RED (IN PHASE)

USED ON
D-190ES
ONLY

WHITE

Positive pressure on diaphragm produces
positive voltage on "in phase" lead.

Polar Diagram

150°   0 dB   150°
        −10
120°   −20   120°
90°   −30   90°
60°   60°
30°   30°

125 Hz   2000 Hz
250 Hz   4000 Hz
500 Hz   8000 Hz
1000 Hz   16,000 Hz

FREQUENCY AND POLAR RESPONSE

~1m (~3-1/4')
ON AXIS

MINIMUM REJECTION AT 180° OFF AXIS.
+3 dB DEVIATION ALLOWABLE WITHIN ANY ONE OCTAVE.

20 Hz   50   100   200   500   1000   2000   5000   10,000 20,000

Fig. 9-3. Technical data for AKG microphones, D-190 series.

good
2 69

popping and annoying breath noises. The D-1000 mike is not only suitable for recording vocals, but enables vocalists to "project" personality in a "live" session.

It comes complete with a built-in on/off switch, a stand adapter, and a padded carrying case. Low- and high-impedance cables are available.

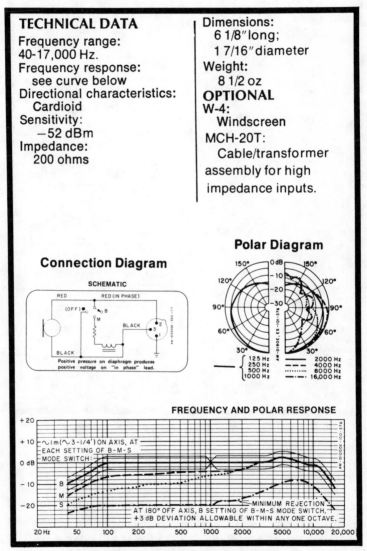

TECHNICAL DATA
Frequency range:
40-17,000 Hz.
Frequency response:
  see curve below
Directional characteristics:
  Cardioid
Sensitivity:
  −52 dBm
Impedance:
  200 ohms

Dimensions:
  6 1/8″long;
  1 7/16″diameter
Weight:
  8 1/2 oz
OPTIONAL
W-4:
  Windscreen
MCH-20T:
  Cable/transformer
assembly for high
impedance inputs.

Connection Diagram

Polar Diagram

Fig. 9-4. Technical data for AKG D-1000 microphone

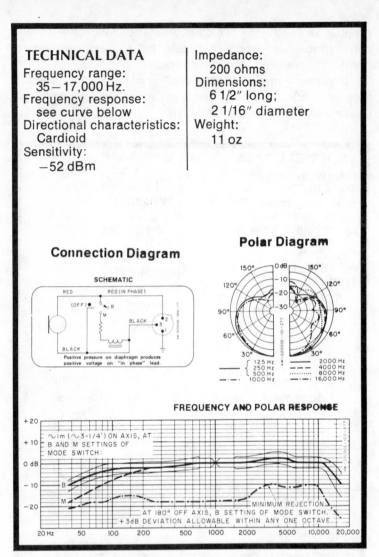

TECHNICAL DATA

Frequency range:
35 – 17,000 Hz.
Frequency response:
see curve below
Directional characteristics:
Cardioid
Sensitivity:
–52 dBm

Impedance:
200 ohms
Dimensions:
6 1/2" long;
2 1/16" diameter
Weight:
11 oz

Connection Diagram

SCHEMATIC

RED   RED (IN PHASE)

(OFF) B
M
BLACK

BLACK

Positive pressure on diaphragm produces
positive voltage on "in phase" lead.

Polar Diagram

```
      125 Hz        2000 Hz
      250 Hz        4000 Hz
      500 Hz        8000 Hz
     1000 Hz        16,000 Hz
```

FREQUENCY AND POLAR RESPONSE

~1m (~3-1/4') ON AXIS, AT
B AND M SETTINGS OF
MODE SWITCH:

B

M

AT 180° OFF AXIS, B SETTING OF MODE SWITCH.
+3dB DEVIATION ALLOWABLE WITHIN ANY ONE OCTAVE.

MINIMUM REJECTION

Fig. 9-5. Technical data for AKG D-2000 microphones.

Technical features of the D-170 series are shown in Fig. 9-5.

Column E in Fig. 9-1 is unusual. Note that this is the only microphone that is suitable for every application. Column E represents the C-500 series of modular electret condenser microphones. The reproduction capabilities of this microphone are far superior to the average cardioid microphone.

Not all condenser mikes are alike, any more than all automobiles are alike, or all people. The C-505E microphone features an internally suspended capsule which eliminates handling noise, and a special design which supplies isolation, and insurance against feedback. It has an integral windscreen to guard against wind noise and popping. And its superb

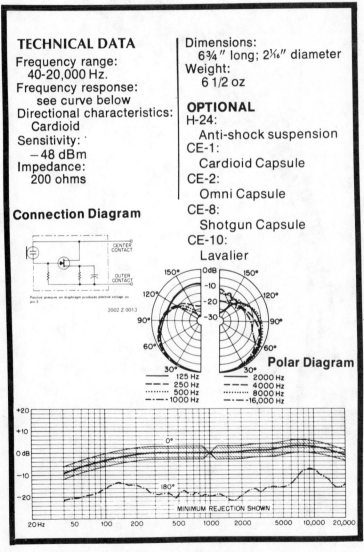

TECHNICAL DATA
Frequency range:
 40-20,000 Hz.
Frequency response:
 see curve below
Directional characteristics:
 Cardioid
Sensitivity:
 −48 dBm
Impedance:
 200 ohms

Dimensions:
 6¾″ long; 2⅙″ diameter
Weight:
 6 1/2 oz

OPTIONAL
H-24:
 Anti-shock suspension
CE-1:
 Cardioid Capsule
CE-2:
 Omni Capsule
CE-8:
 Shotgun Capsule
CE-10:
 Lavalier

Connection Diagram

CENTER CONTACT

OUTER CONTACT

Positive pressure on diaphragm produces positive voltage on pin 2

2002 Z 0013

Polar Diagram

——— 125 Hz
— — — 250 Hz
·········· 500 Hz
—·—·— 1000 Hz

——— 2000 Hz
— — — 4000 Hz
·········· 8000 Hz
—·—·— 16,000 Hz

MINIMUM REJECTION SHOWN

Fig. 9-6. Technical data for AKG C-505 microphone.

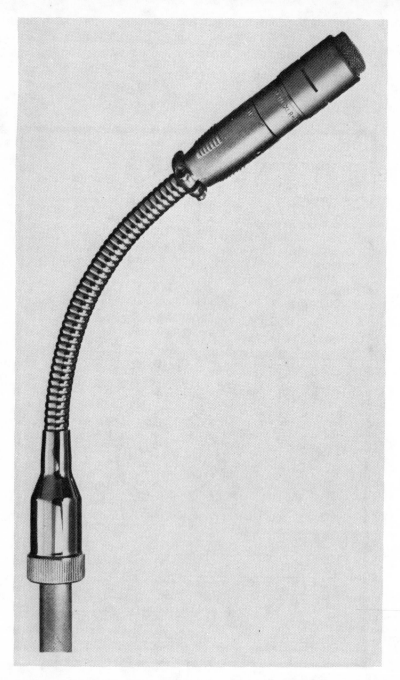

Fig. 9-7. Flexible shaft supplies variety of mike positions.

frequency response makes it an excellent microphone for almost every application.

This series comes complete with a built-in on/off switch, a stand adapter, a padded carrying case, and a battery. Cables are available for both low- and high-impedance operation.

Technical features of the C-505E microphone are shown in Fig. 9-6.

MICROPHONE ACCESSORIES

There are a number of accessories available for use with microphones—a variety of cables, windscreens, suspensions, booms, table stands, stand adapters, flexible shafts, and floor stands, to mention just a few.

The right accessory can be extremely convenient. A flexible shaft, or gooseneck (Fig. 9-7) can change microphone positioning from a nuisance to an easily handled recording situation. The best way to become aware of the accessories that are available is to consult the manufacturer's catalog or to visit your dealer's showroom and discuss your recording problem with your dealer salesman.

Glossary

GLOSSARY

A-B time-intensity stereo—Left/right spaced microphone pair.

AC—Abbreviation for *alternating current*. Also may used to indicate an alternating voltage.

acoustic power output—The total sound power output of a device such as a speaker.

amp—Abbreviation for *amplifier*. Unit can be a pre-amp (preamplifier) or power amp (power amplifier). Amp is also an abbreviation for *ampere*, the basic unit of current.

amplifier—An electronic device for increasing the strength of an electrical signal applied to its input. The electrical signal is AC and is, or should be, an electrical replica of the sound supplied to the microphone. There are two basic types of audio amplifiers: the *preamp*, or voltage amplifier, and the *power* amp, an amplifier capable of delivering relatively large amounts of signal current to a speaker.

attenuator—It is possible to supply a preamp with an excessive amount of signal voltage from a microphone, a condition known as input overload. Some preamps have greater signal input handling capabilities than others. Overload can be controlled by inserting an attenuator, also known as a *loss pad*, or simply as a *pad*, between the microphone and the preamp. The attenuator reduces the amount of microphone signal input to the preamp.

axis—An imaginary line perpendicular to the head of a microphone. Signals that are directed at the head of the microphone are *on axis*. Those that reach the microphone at some angle are *off axis*.

balanced cable—Pair of wires surrounded by metallic shield braid used for connecting the output of a microphone to a preamplifier or to a mixer/preamp.

bar—Unit of sound pressure over a certain area. Corresponds to the dyne per square centimeter (dyne/cm^2).

bass reflex—Ported arrangement in a speaker in which sound energy at the rear of the speaker is permitted to exit from the front in phase with the sound produced by the front of the speaker.

bidirectional microphone—Also known as *figure 8* microphone. Unit has receptivity pattern in the front and rear of the microphone with areas of sound rejection on the sides of the microphone.

bimorph—Dual piezoelectric crystalline structure. Pair of crystal plates cemented together.

boost—An increase in response at some section of a frequency-response curve. Bass boost is an increase in response to low-frequency tones. Treble boost is an increase in response to high-frequency tones. Boost can occur anywhere along the frequency-response curve of a component.

bottoms—Loudspeaker cabinet module with *woofers*. A woofer is speaker designed for bass-range response.

cable—See **balanced cable** and **unbalanced cable**.

carbon microphone—Microphone containing a diaphragm resting against one or two buttons containing carbon granules. Sound pressure on the granules makes the button function as a variable resistor. Current is supplied to the button from a DC source, such as a battery. The resistance variation of carbon granules causes this current to change in step with sound reaching the diaphragm.

cardioid—A type of microphone that picks up sound better from front than back. A heart-shaped response pattern.

ceramic microphone—Microphone that uses barium titanate as its transducing element. Substance has piezoelectric properties, producing a voltage when it is twisted, pressed, or squeezed. Sound exerts pressure on this element, producing the signal output voltage.

condenser microphone—Microphone which depends on the ability of facing conducting surfaces to store an electric charge. Except in cases of electret microphones, condenser microphones require a polarizing voltage, a DC potential ranging from about 50 to 200 volts. The diaphragm is usually flat and can be a metallic substance or metalicized plastic. Separation between the conducting surfaces is about 1 mil (0.001 inch). The signal output is taken from the conducting surfaces and brought directly to an amplifier, generally a part of the microphone.

The condenser microphone can contain one or two diaphragms and a base plate. Variations in the distance between the diaphragm (or diaphragms) and the base plate produces changes in capacitance, resulting in a corresponding variation in output voltage.

cps—Cycle per second. A measurement of the frequency of a wave, now replaced by the *Hertz*.

crystal microphone—Microphone using Rochelle salt as the tranducer. Rochelle salt has piezoelectric properties, producing a voltage when it is subjected to some sort of strain.

decibel—Abbreviated as dB, this is a unit indicating a ratio between two voltages, currents, or powers. Two to three decibels is usually the smallest change in sound level which can be detected by the human ear. An increase of 6 dB means the sound pressure level has doubled. A sound pressure level (SPL) of 0 dB is the threshold of human hearing. It is the lowest SPL of which you can be aware.

diaphragm—Moving element of a microphone. It may be flat, as in the case of condenser microphones, or sometimes convex, as in dynamic microphones.

differential microphone—Also known as a *noise-cancelling microphone*, especially designed for speech communications in high-level noise environments.

directivity—Area or areas of response of a microphone.

double-element microphone—Also called a two-way or coaxial microphone, it uses two microphone elements instead of one, with each designed to cover a particular band of sound frequencies.

dry sound—Primary sound without reverberation. Sound arriving directly from a source, without reflections.

dynamic microphone—A microphone which contains a coil of wire positioned between the poles of a permanent magnet, with the coil fastened to a diaphragm. A moving-coil microphone.

dyne—The *dyne per square centimeter* is a unit of sound pressure.

electret microphone—A condenser microphone using a capacitor-like device, an *electret*, which is precharged by the manufacturer. This eliminates the need for a polarizing voltage, a requirement of ordinary condenser mikes.

element—See **diaphragm**.

feedback—Feedback consists of an electrical or audible signal fed back from some output to an input. The sound produced by a speaker is an output, that going into a microphone is an input. When sound from a speaker is fed back at a high enough level, *in phase*, to a microphone, the result can be ringing or howling.

figure 8—Bilateral frequency response. A microphone response pattern resembling the digit 8.

frequency—Frequency refers to the number of vibrations of sound per second or the number of complete cycles per second of an electrical wave. The number of vibrations per second constitutes the *pitch* of a tone. Frequency is measured in cycles per second (cps) or more recently in Hertz, abbreviated as Hz. The Hertz corresponds to the cycle per second—60 Hz is 60 Hertz or 60 cps.

frequency response—The way in which an electronic device, such as a microphone, amplifier, or speaker responds to signals having a varying frequency. A flat frequency response indicates that the device or component handles signals of all frequencies in the same way, without favoritism. Some components boost certain frequencies or do not respond well to all frequencies.

front-to-back discrimination—Comparison of sound picked up by the front of a microphone compared to that picked up at the rear of that microphone. In the case of a cardioid, the front-to-back discrimination can be as much as 20 dB, indicating that the rear of the microphone is 20 dB less sensitive to pickup of sound than the front of the microphone. This refers to results obtained in an anechoic chamber only.

fuzz box—An amplifier, ordinarily used with an instrument such as an electric guitar, for the production of sounds other than those supplied by the guitar. A distortion-type amplifier.

gain—*Amplification*. An increase in strength or amplitude of a signal. The ratio of output signal level to input signal level.

gain control—Variable element for adjusting the amount of gain, most often a variable resistor. A component for controlling the signal level of a device.

H-pad—An attenuator pad inserted in the line between the output of a microphone and input to an amplifier. So called because of its circuit resemblance to the letter H. A network composed of fixed resistors designed to introduce a predetermined reduction in signal strength, such as 10 dB, 20 dB, etc. H-pads are designed to not interfere with impedance matching between the microphone and amplifier.

harmonics—Waves that are multiples in frequency of a fundamental wave. A second harmonic has twice the frequency of its fundamental, a third harmonic has three times the frequency of its fundamental, and so on. Harmonics are also known as *partials* or *overtones*.

heads—Preamplifiers or mixers. A device that receives signals from microphones.

Hertz—A measure of frequency. Cycles per second or cps.

hypercardioid—A cardioid-type of microphone which has a narrow segment of response toward the rear, but with 90° off-axis response more attenuated than that of the cardioid.

impedance—The opposition of a component, such as a microphone, speaker, or input or output of an amplifier, to the flow of current. Microphones are designated as either low- or high-impedance types. Impedance is measured in ohms and is symbolized by the letter Z. Low impedance or low Z is in a range of approximately 50 to 250 ohms; high impedance or high Z usually means an impedance of 10,000 ohms or more.

input overload distortion—Distortion produced by supplying too strong a signal from the output of a microphone to a preamp. Manufacturers of amplifiers indicate in their specification (spec) sheets the maximum amount of signal the preamplifier can accept before overloading. An excessively strong signal going into a preamp cannot be controlled or reduced by the gain control on the preamp, since such controls are located circuitwise following the input.

k—Abbreviation indicating multiplication by 1000. One kilohertz (1 kHz) is 1000 Hz.

lavaliere microphone—Microphone designed to be worn around the neck or attached via a clip to a shirt or dress.

line-matching transformer—Also known as an *impedance-matching transformer*, or just an *impedance transformer*. It is used to change the impedance of a device from *high* to *low*, or vice versa. Line-matching transformers can be built into the microphone or may be external to it. They can be used to change the output impedance of a microphone from low to high or high to low.

loudness—The subjective impression of the strength of a sound. It is the amount of sound perceived by the ears. Loudness is measured in *sones*. One sone is the subjective loudness of a 1 kHz note whose SPL is 40 dB above a standard reference level.

mel—The subjective unit of *pitch*. (See **pitch**). One thousand (1000) mels is the subjective perception of a 1 kHz tone having an SPL of 40 dB above a reference level of 0 dB, or the threshold of hearing.

millibar—Thousandth of a bar, a unit of sound pressure.

mixer—An electronic component that will accept a number of different signal inputs from microphones, combining them into a single electrical output. Since each of the input signals from the various microphones is adjustable by a control, or a group of controls, on the mixer, the relationship of a single sound to all the other sounds can be adjusted.

monophonic sound system (mono)—A system in which all sound is carried by one channel or path. The system may use a number of microphones, one or more pre- and power amps, and possibly more than one speaker. However, at some point, all the inputs from the various microphones are combined into a single channel. If two or more speakers are used, the sound is divided between them, but all the speakers reproduce the same sound.

moving-coil microphone—See **dynamic microphone**.

noise-canceller microphone—See **differential microphone**.

omni—Abbreviation for an omnidirectional microphone.

omnidirectional—Uniformly responsive to an entire sound field at a particular frequency or a band of frequencies. A microphone capable of responding to sound from all directions.

overtones—See **harmonics**.

pad—See **attenuator**.

partials—See **harmonics**.

phasing or phase—The time relationships, usually of a pair of waves. Two waves, starting at the same time, increasing and decreasing at the same time, and terminating at the same time, are *in phase*. The two waves need not have the same amplitudes. Waves that do not start or stop at the same time are *out of phase*. Waves can be partially or completely out of phase.

piezoelectric—A type of tranducer. A substance, usually crystalline, that produces a voltage when subjected to stress, such as bending or twisting.

pitch—The fundamental or basic tone of a sound, determined by its frequency.

polar pattern—Areas of response of a microphone graphed in polar (circular) form.

polarizing potential—Voltage (EMF) for a condenser microphone for establishing a charge on the plates of the microphone. The DC voltage required for a condenser microphone.

pop filter—Shield positioned above the microphone diaphragm or around the exterior of the microphone to reduce the pressure level of certain vocal sounds which can cause a popping effect. The shield is acoustically transparent and does not interfere with the movement of sound toward the microphone diaphragm.

pop sensitivity—Vocal sounds vary, depending on how they are produced by the lips and tongue. Some, such as words starting with the letters *P*, *F*, or *T*, can result in a popping sound. *Popping* is a short-lived "boominess" in the bass end of the sound spectrum. Not all microphones have the same amount of pop sensitivity.

potential—Voltage or electromotive force (EMF).

preamp—Voltage amplifier connected to the signal output of a microphone. Usually solid-state, incorporating transistors for the amplification of the signal. Can be an individual unit or incorporated in a mixer.

pressure gradient—Difference in acoustic pressure. Difference in sound pressure between the front and back of a microphone element.

proximity effect—The increase in low-frequency response in most cardioid and bidirectional microphones when the microphone is used close to a spherical wave sound source.

pure tone—A fundamental tone only, without harmonics. The tone produced by a tuning fork.

quadraphonic sound system—Sometimes called four-channel sound. At least two microphones are used to record left front and right front sound; two more microphones to pick up geft rear and right rear sound.

Quadraphonic sound can be handled in two general ways on records. In the CD-4 method, the four channels of sound are retained throughout the entire recording and playback process. In another technique the four channels, in recording, are combined into two by a process known as matrixing. In the reproduction process the channels are separated into the original four before reaching the pairs of front and rear speakers. There are a number of suggested matrixing techniques, but the two most widely used are the QS and SQ.

ribbon microphone—Microphone with a metallic ribbon suspended between the poles of a magnet. The movement of the ribbon in the magnetic field provided by the permanent magnet produces a voltage. A microphone functioning on the principle of electromagnetic induction, producing an EMF corresponding to amplitude changes of an incident sound wave. A velocity microphone.

rolloff—A decrease in frequency response at the bass or low-frequency end of a response curve or at the treble or high-frequency end, or at both. Indicated in decibels per octave.

sensitivity—Response of a microphone to sound pressure. The output voltage of microphone given in dB referenced to 1 mW at an SPL of 10 dynes/cm^2 at a specific frequency.

shock mounts—Devices for subduing or eliminating the transfer of mechanical vibrations to the microphone diaphragm. Shock mounts can be external to the microphone or built into it.

shock sensitivity—Reaction of a microphone to handling. The movement of a microphone cable, jarring of a microphone housing, or accidentally hitting it against a hard object can result in microphone sound output. The higher the shock sensitivity of a microphone, the more readily it converts such mechanical shocks to sound.

sibilance—Hissing sound produced when a speaker uses words having S or Z. Sometimes caused by performer speaking directly into a microphone. Correct this condition by talking across the microphone instead of into it, or by using a windscreen.

sone—Subjective loudness of a 1kHz tone at an SPL of 40 dB above the reference level.

sound pressure level—Abbreviated as SPL, it is the deviation above and below normal atmospheric pressure. Atmospheric pressure exists in the presence or absence of sound. Through vibration, voices or musical instruments cause variations in atmospheric pressure. When these variations reach our ears we interpret them as sound.

sound system—System for the reproduction of sound, using one or more microphones. A sound system generally includes, in addition to microphones, devices such as attenuators (also known as pads), preamplifiers, mixers, combined pre-amp/mixers, power amplifiers and speakers. Public sound systems can include other sound sources such as AM/FM broadcasts, phono records or recorded tape.

SPL—Abbreviation for sound pressure level.

standing waves—Sound waves in a room that are in or out of phase. Regions in a room in which there are dead sound spots or very loud sound spots.

stereo condenser microphone—Two complete and separate microphone systems in one body.

stereophonic sound system (stereo)—Sound system with two channels or sound paths. Channels are identified with respect to *dry* sound. Sounds produced from center to left of stage are called left channel; sounds from center to right are called right channel.

supercardioid microphone—A modified cardioid microphone with two lobes, front and rear, but with a rear lobe much smaller than the front. A microphone with an elongated front lobe.

threshold of hearing—Sound level at which sound becomes perceptible to the human ear.

tops—Loudspeaker cabinet modules with midrange or tweeters. Midrange is a speaker that reproduces midrange frequencies; a tweeter is a speaker that reproduces the treble range.

transducer—Device for the conversion of one form of energy to another. All microphones are transducers. So are speakers, motors, and batteries.

transformer—See **line-matching transformer**.

transient—Wave having very short or no sustain time. Wave that starts and stops rapidly. Wave having very short lifetime compared to other waves.

unbalanced cable—Cable consisting of central conductor (wire) surrounded by shield braid.

velocity microphone—See **ribbon microphone**.

windscreen—Shield, for protection against movement of wind or rapid transfer of the microphone from one place to another.

Windscreens generally cover the microphone only partially. The screen only has to cover the end of an omni and is placed over any rear sound holes in the body for directional microphones. Only shotgun and slotted-in-body microphones need screens covering the entire microphone. Such types are rare. Head only screen services the majority of microphone designs.

working distance—Distance from the sound source to the diaphragm of the microphone. Sound pressure input to a microphone decreases by 6 dB when the distance from the performer to the microphone is doubled. 6 dB corresponds to a 4 to 1 ratio, so the sound pressure level drops by this amount every time the distance from the sound source to the microphone is doubled.

X-Y intensity stereo—Microphone pair mounted on a bar with heads almost touching.

Index